PORTRAITS
and
OTHER WORKS OF ART
in the Possession of the
American Philosophical Society

Memoirs of the
AMERICAN PHILOSOPHICAL SOCIETY
Held at Philadelphia
For Promoting Useful Knowledge

Volume 54

Fig. 1. Benjamin Franklin [1]. By Charles Willson Peale, after David Martin

A Catalogue of
PORTRAITS
and
OTHER WORKS OF ART
in the Possession of the
American Philosophical Society

THE AMERICAN PHILOSOPHICAL SOCIETY

INDEPENDENCE SQUARE ● PHILADELPHIA

1961

The research for this Catalogue was carried out by Anna Wells Rutledge. The manuscript was edited and prepared for the printer by Charles Coleman Sellers, of Dickinson College, with the cooperation of the staff of the American Philosophical Society.

Acknowledgment should also be made of assistance rendered by the following individuals: William Billington, of the Wedgwood Museum, Barlaston, England; Harry M. Buten, of the Buten Museum of Wedgwood, Merion, Pennsylvania; Francis James Dallett, of the Athenaeum of Philadelphia; Ulysse Desportes, of Hollins College; Miss Agnes Mongan, of the Fogg Museum; Lucien Scheler, of the Librairie Thomas-Scheler, Paris.

Copyright © 1961 by the American Philosophical Society

Library of Congress Catalogue
Card Number: 61-14631

Preface

The portrait collection of the Society had its beginning on January 16, 1785, with Charles Willson Peale's gift of a portrait of Benjamin Franklin, "copied from a much-admired painting of Martin." The members, in returning their thanks, requested that he keep the picture until they should have "a convenient place for its reception." Like family portraits, which they resemble in so many ways, the portraits of an institution are inevitably associated with the idea of a home. At the time of Peale's gift the Society for some months had been actively raising funds for the erection of Philosophical Hall. Four years later, July 17, 1789, with the Hall completed and removal into it imminent, the members voted a new portrait of Franklin, to be painted by Peale and "to be perpetually kept in one of their apartments." Peale was not present at the meeting and his earlier gift had been forgotten. The outcome of this misunderstanding was that the earlier portrait, after Martin, was hung in the Hall, and that Peale, two years later, was commissioned to add another of the President who had succeeded Franklin, David Rittenhouse. Others followed slowly. That of Washington, voted at the meeting of December 27, 1799, was received from the artist, Gilbert Stuart, April 15, 1803. Characteristically, it seems to have been John Vaughan who first conceived the idea of a gallery, regularly maintained as a symbolic union of past and present, and who set the project in motion. At the meeting of July 16, 1830, he announced that "several of the members had made arrangements to procure portraits of the several Presidents of the Society for the purpose of offering them to its acceptance." A resolution followed authorizing the President and the Librarian to borrow "such portraits of our deceased Presidents as may be deemed the best for the purpose of being copied." Today every President until very recent years is represented, with the addition also of many other officers and distinguished members.

This catalogue is the collection's first systematic appraisal as documents of the past and as works of art. Each item has been photographed, described, and its history studied. The archives of the Society have been searched thoroughly for pertinent facts, as have the resources of sister institutions, notably the Athenaeum of Philadelphia, the Historical Society of Pennsylvania, and the Library Company. Material of great value, much of it beyond the scope of this catalogue, has been discovered and recorded. The Society's manuscript collections have been found to contain not only documentation but original works of the greatest interest to art historians and these, though not listed here, have received due attention. Among them are many small portrait drawings—Benjamin Franklin Bache's sketch of his grandfather, a Peale profile of Washington in medallic design, a vivid, unfinished water color of Lieutenant Colonel William Washington attributed to Charles Willson Peale and painted, apparently, when the hero came to receive the laurels of his dashing charge and victory at the Cowpens, Peale's sketches of the wan features of his dying brother, Saint George, and a wash drawing after Sir Henry Raeburn of the Scottish judge, artist and wit, John Clerk, Lord Eldin. Objects of this sort, with the Society's portrait photograph collection, its large collection of engravings and its coins and medals, may be found recorded elsewhere.

This catalogue lists the paintings and sculpture to be seen in Hall and Library, both the "family portraits" of this institution, and the formal works of art on view there. In its portraits, as John Kintzing Kane put it in his *Eulogium* on Simeon DeWitt, the membership expected "not a eulogy but a record." Each, he said, "is a family portrait in which the survivors may well prefer exact fidelity of delineation to the most brilliant colours, or the fullest evidence of pictorial skill." All the subjects here listed are members of the Society with the exceptions of twelve, Boyle, Copernicus, Cuvier, Ferrero, Mrs. Franklin, Jones, Napier, Newton, Penn, Turgot, Wellington, and the portrait of Shahaka, the American Indian, and these in diverse other ways represent the interests of the membership. The portraits demonstrate all levels of skill of painter or sculptor, working from life or as copyists. They range from the work of Charles Willson Peale, Stuart, Rush, Houdon, and Ceracchi through Rembrandt Peale to the Bush-Browns, R. Tait McKenzie, Henry Breckenridge, Julian Story, and Thomas Eakins (a portrait after a photograph, a thing unusual with him). It was as Charles C. Harrison said during the presentation of that portrait of Daniel Garrison Brinton by Eakins, "We want to remember not only how he thought and spoke, but how he appeared to us when full of that earnest vigorous life which took such hold upon his friends." This, then, is a portrait gallery essentially of subject

vi

interest, but the eminence of its subjects and the presence among them of artists of note has given it, as art, well-founded aspects of importance.

A list of the artists follows the subject catalogue.

In the preparation of this work the identity of both subject and artist has been studied thoroughly in each instance and, in so far as was possible, confirmed. New attributions and even new identifications of subject have emerged. Thus, for instance, a bust of "Dr. Benjamin Rush" was found to be, actually, a unique portrait of Charles Thomson, Secretary of the Continental Congress. Another, which has posed for years as "Dr. William Smith," became the Rt. Rev. William White, his lawn sleeves clearly marking his episcopal office. Simeon DeWitt was found to have been passing as "De Witt Clinton," and "Simeon De-Witt" has become "Unknown Man." It is appropriate here to recall that the founder of the Society had himself once given his attention to just such an inquiry, and to glance at the line of thought he followed. To Lord Kames, who had sent him a portrait of "William Penn," Franklin wrote as follows on January 3, 1760:

I could wish to know the history of the picture before it came into your hands, and the grounds for supposing it his. I have at present some doubts about it; first, because the primitive Quakers used to declare against pictures as a vain expence; a man's suffering his portrait to be taken was conceived as pride; and I think to this day it is very little practiced among them. Then, it is on a board; and I imagine the practice of painting portraits on boards, did not come down so low as Penn's time; but of this I am not certain. My other reason is, an anecdote I have heard, viz. That when old Lord Cobham was adorning his gardens at Stowe with the busts of famous men, he made inquiry of the family, for the picture of William Penn, in order to get a bust formed from it, but could find none.... I doubt, too, whether the whisker was not quite out of use when Penn must have been of an age appearing in the face of that picture. And yet, notwithstanding these reasons, I am not without some hope that it may be his; because I know some eminent Quakers have had their pictures privately drawn and deposited with trusty friends. (Smyth, *Writings of Benjamin Franklin* 4: 5–6, 1905–1907.)

The portrait is known through a copy now owned by the Independence National Historical Park. Both with Franklin's doubts as to the subject, and with his method of inquiry, the modern scholar would heartily agree. Provenance, technique, apparent age of subject and other evidence within the picture, its relationship to social custom, inquiry into other portraits

vii

of the supposed subject, all these are basic elements of the art historian's task. They are echoed in this study of the Society's collections, the detailed findings of which are preserved in the Library, and the conclusions published here.

The arrangement is alphabetical, the *portraits* by *subject*, and the smaller number of *other works* under the name of the *artist*.

All quotations, unless otherwise identified, are from sources in the Library of the American Philosophical Society.

The Library's accession number appears at the close of each entry. This has no relation to the numbers added for convenience to the headings where more than one portrait of an individual is listed.

The date following the abbreviation APS at the beginning of each account is the date of election to membership in the American Philosophical Society. This is followed by the dates of any offices held in the Society.

Dimensions are given in inches, height before width.

Catalogue

JOHN QUINCY ADAMS [1], 1767–1848 (Fig. 36)

Statesman. Sixth President of the United States.
APS 1818; Councillor 1819–1831.

In a letter from Washington, April 23, 1818, Adams acknowledged his election to the American Philosophical Society, adding,

It is among the most gratifying Events of my Life to be associated with men and with Institutions devoted to the pursuits of Literature and Science; pursuits from which however withheld by unremitted and indispensible occupations, my affections can never be estranged.

On November 23 of the following year he acknowledged with gratitude that the Library of the Society had been of service to him "in the preparation of a Report required by the Senate of the United States." In the interval he had posed to a little-known sculptor, Pietro Cardelli, employed in decorative work on the capitol. Cardelli, during his brief residence in the area, also made busts of Jefferson and Madison. Excerpts from Adams' diary give the only documentation of Cardelli's portrait of him:

July 5, 1818
Cardelli was here this morning.

July 19, 1818
Cardelli came, and I gave him a second sitting for the bust. He says everything in my head is difficult for a bust, which I can well understand.

July 26, 1818
Cardelli was here and I gave him the third and last sitting for the bust.

August 9, 1818
Cardelli was here great part of the day. He had finished the bust, but we found that he had totally failed in the likeness; so he asked for another sitting which I gave him; he altered it very much but will ultimately not get a likeness.

August 16, 1818
Cardelli came, and cast the hollow mould, the creux perdu of the bust. I had never seen and had no idea of the manner of casting Statues in Plaster. There is nothing in the work that can properly be

1

called Sculpture. The first mould is taken in soft red clay worked by the hand, the second is this Plaister Shell moulded over it in two halves. The Bust itself is cast in this, and must be done hereafter. Cardelli dined with us.

August 23, 1818
Cardelli came and cast the bust, and afterwards dined with us. (Adams Papers, Massachusetts Historical Society.)

The portrait, of the success of which its subject was at one juncture so pointedly in doubt, was presented to the Society on February 20, 1829, the closing year of Adams' presidential administration.

By Pietro Cardelli, 1818.
Plaster bust. Height 23¾".
Gift of Dr. John Kearsley Mitchell, 1829.
(58.S.15)

JOHN QUINCY ADAMS [2]

The Minutes on January 20, 1832, carried, "D. Harlan, on behalf of Mr. S. J. Wetherill, presented, a cast Iron bust of John Q. Adams, cast at Windsor Furnace, Bucks County."

Unlocated.

LOUIS JEAN RODOLPHE AGASSIZ, 1807–1873 (Fig. 45)

Naturalist.
APS 1843.
The Society's portrait of Agassiz comes from a climactic year in his life, marking both his fiftieth birthday and the completion of the first volume of his monumental *Contributions to the Natural History of the United States,* a project to which he had passionately devoted his life. His students joined in honoring him as the applause of the public and the learned world poured in. Longfellow, presiding at a Saturday Club dinner, read his poem, *The Fiftieth Birthday of Agassiz,* in which Nature addresses him as her son:

> "Come, wander with me," she said,
> "Into regions yet untrod;
> And read what is still unread
> In the manuscripts of God."

Here, in his own tribute, an outstanding artist of the time has captured this moment of triumph, and with it the robust and handsome figure, the pervasive, dominant friendliness. Here is the man who, as William James said many years later when Harvard celebrated the fiftieth anniversary of Agassiz's arrival in

2

America, "stands forth immediately as a scientific leader of men. . . . He elevated the popular notion of what a student of Nature should be. Since Benjamin Franklin, we had never had among us a person of more popularly impressive type."

By Daniel Huntington, 1857.
Oil on canvas. $30\frac{1}{4}'' \times 25\frac{1}{4}''$.
Signed (lower left): "Agassiz / by D. Huntington / 1857."
Gift of John Frederick Lewis, Jr. 1934.
(58.P.47)

The Eclipse of June 16, 1806. By EZRA AMES.

The Minutes of May 15, 1807, record the receipt from Simeon DeWitt ($q.v.$) of a paper "On the Sun's Eclipse, observed at Albany, June 16, 1806," and with it a painting of the occurrence. The donor's letter, dated Albany, April 25, 1807, presented the picture to the Society in the following terms:

With this I send you for the American Philosophical Society a painting intended to represent the central Eclipse of the Sun on the 16th of last June. It is executed by Mr. Ezra Ames an eminent painter of this place and gives I believe as true a representation of that grand and beautiful Phenomenon as can be artificially represented. The Edge of the moon was strongly illuminated and had the brilliancy of polished silver. No common colors express this; I therefore directed it to be attempted as you see by a raised silver rim which in a proper light produces tolerably well the intended effect.

As no verbal description can give any thing like a true Idea of this Sublime Spectacle with which man is so rarely gratified, I thought this painting would not be an unwelcome present to the Society or an improper Article to be preserved among its collection of Subjects for philosophical Speculation. But in order to have a proper conception of what is intended to be represented you must transfer your Ideas to the Heavens, and imagine, at the departure of the last ray of the Sun in its retreat behind the moon and awful gloom immediately diffused over the face of Nature, and round a dark circle near the Zenith an immense radiated GLORY like a New Creation in a Moment bursting on the Sight and for several minutes fixing the Gaze of Man in Silent amazement.

By Ezra Ames, 1806.
Oil on [canvas?].
Gift of Simeon DeWitt, 1807.
Unlocated.

ALEXANDER DALLAS BACHE, 1806–1867 (Fig. 41)

Physicist, educator.
APS 1829; Secretary 1833–1845; Vice-President 1845–1855; President 1855–1857.

3

On June 6, 1862, Alexander Dallas Bache wrote from Washington to J. Peter Lesley at the Society, "Mr. Huntington of New York has put me upon canvas & I should be glad to deposit the picture in the old Hall if it would be acceptable."

The picture was then on exhibition at the National Academy of Design in New York. Its painter was first elected President of the Academy in that year. Its subject was the first President of the National Academy of Sciences, one of the original Regents of the Smithsonian Institution and Superintendent of the United States Coast Survey. He was a great-grandson of Benjamin Franklin and, gifted with Franklin's broad administrative ability, was acknowledged in America and Europe as one of the great scientists and educators of his time.

By Daniel Huntington, 1861.
Oil on canvas. $36\frac{1}{8}'' \times 29\frac{1}{8}''$.
Signed (lower right): "D. Huntington / 1861."
Gift of Alexander Dallas Bache, 1862.
(58.P.40)

FRANKLIN BACHE, 1792–1864

Chemist, physician, pharmaceutist.

APS 1820; Secretary 1825–1843; Vice-President 1843–1853; President 1853–1855.

Painted posthumously, Dr. Bache's portrait was commissioned as a monument both to his close relationship to the Society and to his contributions to chemistry carried out as teacher, author, and editor. It was upon his motion in 1858 (after he had previously refused to allow his name on the ballot) that the by-law limiting the term of President of the Society was repealed. He was long on the Historical and Literary Committee, and decisions on the sorting and binding of the Franklin manuscripts were largely his. He gave both advice and funds for the advancement of the Library. His 1819 *System of Chemistry for the Students of Medicine* was followed by successive editions of Turner's *Chemistry* and his revision of the *United States Pharmacopoeia*. With Dr. George Bacon Wood (*q.v.*) he revised the *United States Dispensatory* of 1833, editing thereafter the eleven editions which appeared in his lifetime. He was a great-grandson of Benjamin Franklin, and Thomas Jefferson, in a letter of May 17, 1824, praises him for "applying science to the utilities of life," and giving it "that high merit for which your illustrious ancestor was so distinguished." Four years after his death, the Society's Minutes carried:

4

June 19, 1868

On motion of Mr. Peale—Resolved that a Committee be appointed to have a portraite of Dr. Franklin Bache late president of the Society, painted for the Society. Mr. Peale was appointed to be said committee to carry this Resolution into effect.

October 2, 1868

The portrait of Dr. Franklin Bache, late president of this Society, recently painted by Mr. Waugh of Philadelphia, on the order of a special committee of the Society, was exhibited for the inspection of the members present.

November 6, 1868

Mr. Peale moved an appropriation of $131.60 to pay for the picture (and frame) of Dr. Franklin Bache, which was made, and The Committee discharged.

November 20, 1868

Mr. Peale explained an error in the call for an appropriation recently made to pay for Dr. Bache's portrait, and asked for the appropriation of one hundred dollars, which was, on motion, granted.

By Samuel Bell Waugh, 1868, probably after a photograph by F. Gutekunst.
Oil on canvas. 30¼" × 25".
Signed (lower right): "S. B. Waugh 1868."
Painted on order, 1868.
(58.P.27)

SPENCER FULLERTON BAIRD, 1823–1887

Zoologist, ornithologist, ichthyologist. Second Secretary of the Smithsonian Institution.

APS 1855.

Baird's portrait commemorates a life of unusual energy and breadth. In 1850, at the age of twenty-seven, he resigned his professorship at Dickinson College to become Assistant Secretary of the new Smithsonian Institution. He followed Joseph Henry as Secretary in 1878. As first head of the United States Commission of Fish and Fisheries, he organized its activities and its headquarters at Woods Hole. The National Museum, founded in 1876, was largely his personal creation. His influence in exploration, ethnological study, and all the natural sciences was central and pervasive. Information sent by him to Congress was a deciding factor in the purchase of Alaska. His publications exceed a thousand, and more than fifty thousand of his letters remain as witness to his world-wide interests and activity, as well as to friendships and public admiration within as wide a range. On March 7, 1890, the Society

Resolved that a Committee be appointed by the President to examine an oil portrait of Prof. S. F. Baird, by Mr. H. Ulke, report on its desirability, and if favorably, to solicit subscriptions for its purchase at a price not exceeding $200, for the gallery of this Society.

Reports followed at the meetings of March 21, May 2, May 16, and at that of December 19, 1890:

Dr. Horn, from the Committee to obtain for the Society the Portrait of S. F. Baird, by Ulke, reported that it had been purchased and was now on the walls of the meeting room, and read a list of the donors for its purchase.

By Henry Ulke, 1887, perhaps after a photograph.
Oil on canvas. 30" × 25".
Signed (lower right): "H. Ulke. 1887."
Gift of members and friends, among whom were Harrison Allen, John R. Baker, W. S. Baker, George F. Barker, Arthur Biddle, David G. Brinton, Thomas M. Cleeman, Frederick Fraley, George H. Horn, Edwin J. Houston, Horace Jayne, T. S. Kendall, J. Peter Lesley, George R. Morehouse, J. Chester Morris, Robert Patterson, William John Potts, J. Sergeant Price, W. S. W. Ruschenberger, Lewis A. Scott, William P. Tatham, Richard Vaux, Samuel Wagner, Richard Wood, and Joseph G. Rosengarten; also the Misses Emily and Ellen Phillips and Henry Ulke, the artist, 1890.
(58.P.11)

SIR JOSEPH BANKS, 1744–1820

Naturalist, munificent patron of botany and biological exploration.
APS 1787.
A rich man with a passion for botany, Sir Joseph was President of the Royal Society of London for forty-two years, devoting much of his time and fortune to the welfare of the Society. He accompanied Captain James Cook on his first voyage of discovery in the *Endeavour* to observe the transit of Venus in the Pacific in 1769.

By Wedgwood, *circa* 1905. Modeled by A. H. Bentley after John Flaxman's model of 1779.
Ceramic plaque. White on green jasper dip. 12⅛" × 8 9/16".
Inscribed in relief on the field: "SIR JOSEPH BANKS." Impressed on back: "WEDGWOOD / o."
Provenance unknown.
(58.S.46)

6

The American Union (Fig. 59). By FRANÇOIS, MARQUIS DE BARBÉ-MARBOIS

François Barbé de Marbois, afterward François, Marquis de Barbé-Marbois, came to America in 1779 with the French minister, Luzerne, as secretary of legation. He remained, as *chargé-d'affaires* and consul-general, until 1785. Later, as a statesman of the Napoleonic empire, he had a part in the negotiations leading to the Louisiana Purchase. In Philadelphia he figured as a gay and graceful leader of the city's social life. This spirit he brought also to the meetings of the Society, to which he had been elected soon after his arrival. Elected a Councillor on January 5, 1781, he was called to preside at the meeting of March 15 as "the *eldest councillor* present" (he was then thirty-six years of age). Peter Stephen Du Ponceau remembered him especially for his musical talent—"M. de Marbois, the Secretary of Legation, played a good violin." Nowhere, however, is he remembered or recorded as an artist, and his signature on the Society's unique drawing is in such form as to indicate that it was he who conceived the design, but that it was actually carried out by an unknown professional draughtsman.

This work, *The American Union,* celebrates the ratification by Congress of the definitive treaty of peace between the United States and Great Britain, January 14, 1784. It was probably intended as the design for an engraving to be published in honor of the event, though the occasion passed without such commemoration. The earliest actual documentation of the drawing occurs in the Society's Minutes of December 15, 1841:

From Mr. William Amies, dated Philadelphia, 10th Dec. 1841, making a donation to the Society of a painting emblematic of the American Union, executed in 1784, by order of M. Barbé de Marbois, and by him presented to Charles Thomson, Secretary of the American Congress; together with a copy of the Resolution of that Congress, passed 14th Jan. 1784, authenticated by Charles Thomson.

Mr. Amies' letter of December 10, addressed to Peter S. Du Ponceau, gives no specific facts, stating only that "Its endorsement will give you its history." The phrase, "executed in 1784, by order of M. Barbé de Marbois," confirms the statement implicit in the signature. "Marbois Invenit" claims only the idea, not the execution. Had the latter been true the signature would have read, "Marbois Delineavit."

The drawing, in addition to its character as a tribute of admiration from France to America, has had also the effect of establishing Pennsylvania as "The Keystone State." In the arch upon which the figure of Hercules stands it is quite obvious

7

that the states have simply been named in geographical order, and that Pennsylvania is only in the center by virtue of having six others to the north, and six to the south. However, on June 4, 1788, John Vaughan, to whom this little work was of course familiar, wrote to his brother Benjamin Vaughan of the progress of the ratification of the new constitution, ". . . and I hope soon to hand you the 9th Confirmation which will be the Keystone to the Arch." There can be little doubt that the phrase and the general use of the symbolism originated with this popular and active adopted son of the commonwealth.

By François, Marquis de Barbé-Marbois, 1784.
Ink and water color on paper. $11\frac{7}{8}'' \times 8\frac{5}{8}''$.
Signed (lower left): "Marbois Invenit."
Gift of William Amies, 1841.
(58.P.86)

NICHOLAS BIDDLE, 1786–1844

Statesman, financier, *litterateur*.
APS 1813; Councillor 1831–1843.
His bust portrays with the classic simplicity he so deeply loved both the gentleman and scholar and the serenity he maintained in the midst of stormy controversy. As President of the Bank of the United States he had done much to maintain the financial stability of the nation, and had proved personally impervious to the attacks upon it. He had been Secretary to General Armstrong in France and present at the coronation of Napoleon in 1804, had traveled as far as Greece, had served as Secretary to Legation at London before returning to America in 1807. Although called first to the bar and then to banking, his preference was for active work in literature. He was a member of the "Tuesday Club" group which helped to make the *Port Folio* America's foremost literary magazine. He gave much time to arranging the journals of the Lewis and Clark Expedition into a *History . . .* (1814). On April 6, 1818, he wrote to William Tilghman,

I have the pleasure of depositing with the Historical Committee the papers and books which accompany this letter, in compliance with the request of Govenor Clark in his letter to me of the 10th of October 1816 transmitted by Mr. Jefferson.

It was he who delivered the Society's "Eulogium" on its late President, Thomas Jefferson, in 1827. In 1839 he retired to his beloved "Andalusia" on the Delaware River.

8

Attributed to E. Luigi Persico.
Plaster bust. Height 21⅜".
Provenance unknown.
(58.S.14)

Fairmount Water Works (Fig. 57). By THOMAS BIRCH

The public improvements at Fairmount, pride of the city of Philadelphia and a perennially popular subject with its artists, were begun in 1812 and completed after ten years of effort in December, 1822. The engineer in charge was Frederick Graff (1775–1847), who had been trained in the office of Benjamin H. Latrobe, builder of the older water works in Center Square, a site which had been in its day equally attractive to painters. Thomas Birch exhibited a view of Fairmount at the Pennsylvania Academy of the Fine Arts in 1824. In this work, which shows the costumes of that period, the scene is depicted from the westward, above the Upper Ferry Bridge.

By Thomas Birch, *circa* 1824.
Oil on canvas. 13" × 18¾".
Bequest of Adolph G. Rosengarten, 1948.
(58.P.85)

NATHANIEL BOWDITCH, 1773–1839 (Fig. 33)

Seaman, mathematician, astronomer.
APS 1809.

Bowditch's *New Practical Navigator* was published in 1799, and his *New American Practical Navigator* (still in use) first appeared in 1802. On August 1, 1809, he wrote from his home in Salem, Massachusetts, to the Corresponding Secretary acknowledging his election as a member of the Society:

I would thank you to express to the Society the high sense I have of the honour conferred on me by this distinguished mark of their attention, and to inform them that it would always be gratifying to me to assist in any way in promoting the laudable and important objects of the institution.

I have sent by this conveyance a small paper on Spherics (just printed in the Memoirs of the American Academy of Arts and Sciences). The object of this essay is to suggest an alteration in the celebrated rules of Napier, so as to include Oblique Spherical Trigonometry in a more simple manner than in their original form. Also a chart of the harbours of Salem, Marblehead, Beverly, and Manchester, with a book of directions, made from a survey of those places, with great care, much labour, and considerable expense. You will be good enough to present these papers to the Society, with

9

my best wishes for their continued success in their present useful pursuits for the improvement of science.

Thirty years later the Society received a letter from the artist, dated March 1, 1839, at 66 South Sixth Street, Philadelphia:

May I be pardoned the liberty of offering for your Society a Bust of the late distinguished Dr. Bowditch, of Boston?
The likeness has been approved by the family, and I have the privilege of disposing of the cast if you would like to possess it. The price is fifteen dollars without or twenty dollars with the pedestal.
I need not say how proud I should be to have a work of mine in your room, more particularly as it is already adorned with Busts by Flaxman and Chantry.

The Minutes for March 1, 1839, carried, "On motion of Mr. Vaughan, it was resolved that the bust of Dr. Bowditch, offered this evening in the letter of Mr. Hughes for $15, be purchased by the Society."

Cast after Robert Ball Hughes' bust of *circa* 1837.
Plaster bust. Height 26″.
Cast in shoulder: "DOCTOR BOWDITCH / EXECUTED IN MARBLE / BY BALL HUGHES / FOR THE / SOCIETY OF ARTS / AND SCIENCES / BOSTON." On sculptured book forming base:" "TRAITE DE MECANIQUE CELESTE / of La Place."
Purchased 1839.
(58.S.4)

MARTIN HANS BOYÉ, 1812–1909

Chemist, physicist, geologist.
APS 1840.

A graduate of the University of Copenhagen, Boyé came to the United States in 1836. In 1844 he received the degree of Doctor of Medicine at the University of Pennsylvania. Among his achievements was the refinement in 1845 of cotton seed into a bland oil suitable for cooking and salad dressing as well as soap. An 1848 sample of this oil received the first premium at the Philadelphia Centennial Exposition of 1876. In 1904 the Society gave him a "rising vote" as its oldest living member. A legacy from his will was in 1910 assigned to the purchase of books on chemistry and geology.

By an unidentified artist, probably after a photograph, *circa* 1898.
Crayon on paper. 23¾″ × 20″.
Provenance unknown.
(58.P.87)

10

ROBERT BOYLE, 1627–1691

Natural philosopher, chemist, theologian. Propounder of "Boyle's Law" defining the relation between pressure and volume of gases. One of the founders of the Royal Society of London.

By Wedgwood, *circa* 1905. Modeled by A. H. Bentley after a model supplied by the firm of James Hoskins and Benjamin Grant, *circa* 1775.
Ceramic plaque. White on green jasper dip. 12″ × 8½″.
Inscribed in relief on the field: "Boyle." Impressed on back: "Wedgwood / o."
Provenance unknown.
(58.S.44)

DANIEL GARRISON BRINTON, 1837–1899 (Fig. 47)

Physician, anthropologist, ethnologist.
APS 1869; Curator 1877–1880; Secretary 1880–1896.

Dr. Brinton was a scientist in whom the Society's position in the humanities was also represented. His medical background was both American and European. He was widely read in English and continental literature, was one of the first to recognize the genius of Whitman, and one of the first to maintain that the American Indian possesses a literature and literary history. On his retirement from medicine he held the Chair of American Archaeology and Linguistics at the University of Pennsylvania, where his unique library of books and manuscripts is now preserved. His portrait was presented, January 16, 1900, at a joint meeting of the twenty-six learned societies of which he had been a member. On this occasion Provost Harrison of the University spoke of the need "to remember not only how he thought and spoke, but how he appeared to us when full of that vigorous life which took such hold upon his friends." Formal presentation of the portrait was made by the Honorable Samuel W. Pennypacker, who said:

Some friends, not unmindful of the importance of contributions to science made by Dr. Brinton, and anxious that his lineaments may be preserved for future generations, have had this portrait painted by a distinguished artist, Mr. Thomas Eakins. The situation and surroundings are all propitious and fitting. In this Hall are collected the records of that sect which founded the province and to which the ancestors of Dr. Brinton belonged. The picture itself is a representation of that art in which Sir [*sic*] Benjamin West, born in the neighborhood where the family Brinton lived, reached the highest distinction of his time. . . .

11

Professor J. W. Holland, M.D., responded:

On behalf of the American Philosophical Society, I have the honor to accept this most appropriate gift and express to the donors our grateful acknowledgment. In paying my tribute of admiration for the skill of the artist, I am reminded that he studied human anatomy at the same school, though not at the same time with Dr. Brinton. In that college of medicine young Brinton, at a plastic age, felt the formative influence of teachers who were members of the American Philosophical Society.... When he turned aside from medical studies to cultivate the new ground of American archaeology and linguistics it was the Philosophical Society that he brought the rich harvest of his labors. In its transactions are garnered the ripe fruits of his research....

Sir, your gift of the portrait of the patriot Surgeon, the man of light and leading, the learned archaeologist, will be placed in the goodly fellowship of our departed worthies, a fit companion to the portraits of Jefferson and Franklin.

By Thomas Eakins, *circa* 1899, perhaps after a photograph. Oil on canvas. 30″ × 25″. Gift of friends, 1900. (58.P.39)

DAVID STEWART ERSKINE, EARL OF BUCHAN, 1742–1829

Amateur antiquarian, artist. APS 1794.

George Washington, with whom he claimed relationship, was one of the Earl's many noted correspondents, and it was Washington who proposed him for membership in the Society. In 1792 he had sent Washington a snuff box made from the tree which had sheltered William Wallace. On January 12, 1795, he wrote to David Rittenhouse from his estate, Dryburgh Abbey, in Scotland:

Sir,

My worthy friend Mr. John Millar son of the eminent Professor John Millar of Glasgow whom I recommend to your attention has charged himself with this letter and will deliver to you a writing box which I dedicate to your use as President of the Philosophical Society at Philadelphia & to your Successors in Office as a Testimony of my high esteem for your Literary Character and for that of the Society over which you preside.

This Box is made of Yew, of Black Cherry Tree, Acacia, and Berberry and veneered with Holly all of the growth of my Garden at this place and joined, fitted, & finished by my own Joiner in this House.

12

On the Lid is an authentic picture of Copernicus [*q.v.*], and in the inside thereof is a similar one of Napier [*q.v.*]. That of Copernicus is from the accurate copy of the Chancellor Hussarzewski's original Picture wch was sent by the learned Dr. Wolf of Dantzic to the Royal Society of London & this limning of mine is most faithfully delineated & shaded from a drawing made by Mr. Thomas Parke of Piccadilly formerly a pupil of Valentine Green Engraver at London from the Picture in the Royal Society on a Scale proportional in all parts and with great fidelity, so that I can assure you of my limning being a Fac simile as to the features & countenance.

That of Napier is indeed a most exquisitely beautiful piece by John Brown of Edr. executed with black lead Pencil from an original Portrait in the possession of Lord Napier; & as a drawing with black Lead excells I believe everything of the kind now extant, Mr. Brown having by drawing during Twelve Years in Italy from Statues obtained a super-eminent accuracy & beauty of design. I consecrate this interesting piece of Furniture to American Science & to the Philosophical Society of Philadelphia, willing however that in consideration of the high Esteem I bear to you Personally you should have the custody & use of it, in your own House during your Life, producing it only to the Society for the use of the Secretary when you think proper. I have subjoined by way of Postscript to this letter some particulars relating to the residence of Copernicus & his Tomb which I wish you to communicate to *our* Society.

. . .

P.S. Upon the whole it appears that the likeness I send of Copernicus is most to be depended on, and that as such I flatter myself it will be an *Heir Loom* to Infant America!

Concerning Napier it is needless for me to enlarge—the learned Dr. Minto having enabled me to do justice to his Memory.

By James Tassie, 1783.

Paste bas-relief, mounted on marble. Height 2⅞″ (marble 4″ × 2¾″, sight).

Inscribed under shoulder: "D. S. BUCHAN COMES / 1783." A note attached to the frame reads: "To the Philosophical Society / at Philadelphia as a Testimony of my Respect / Buchan."

Gift of the Earl of Buchan, 1795.

(58.S.52)

MATHEW CAREY, 1760–1839

Publisher, economist.

APS 1821.

Carey's portrait depicts a turbulent, vigorous, learned man, eloquent, gifted and eager in controversy. A native of Dublin, a

13

writer supporting Irish liberty, he had served Franklin at Passy during the American Revolution. When he emigrated to Philadelphia in 1784, he came provided by Lafayette with funds for the establishment of a newspaper, the beginning of the Carey publishing enterprises. The energy, sense, and information in his writings made him widely known. He shares credit with Alexander Hamilton for giving content and form to the American nationalist school of economic thought. Quick and vituperative in argument as he was, his *Olive Branch, or Faults on Both Sides* became an American best-seller and drew an accolade from Thomas Jefferson, writing from "Poplar Forest," near Lynchburg, October 11, 1816:

> I received here (where I pass a good deal of my time) your favor of Oct. 22, covering a Prospectus of a new edition of your Olive branch: I subscribe to it with pleasure. I believe it has done & will do much good, in holding up the mirror to both parties, and exhibiting to both their political errors. That I have had my share of them, I am not vain enough to doubt.

By T. Henry Smith, 1844, after John Neagle's portrait of *circa* 1825. Oil on canvas. 30″ × 25″.
Signed (lower left): "T. Henry Smith / after / John Neagle / 1844."
Gift of the Hon. Henry Carey Baird, 1893.
(58.P.19)

NATHANIEL CHAPMAN [1], 1780–1853

Physician, medical educator.

APS 1807; Secretary 1808–1814; 1815–1817; Councillor 1817–1828; Vice-President 1828–1846; President 1846–1849.

A Virginian who had studied medicine with Benjamin Rush, and had settled again in Philadelphia after taking his degree at the University of Edinburgh, Dr. Chapman was remembered for his courtly manners, his wit and literary taste as well as for his high professional standing. He was author and editor of medical texts, and Professor of the Theory and Practice of Medicine at the University of Pennsylvania. In 1817 he founded the first post-graduate medical school in this country, which held summer courses for twenty years. He was first President of the American Medical Association.

Attributed to E. Luigi Persico, *circa* 1825.
Plaster bust. Height 23¼″.
Gift of Dr. Samuel Jackson, 1830.
(58.S.17)

NATHANIEL CHAPMAN [2] (Fig. 31)

The Minutes of January 19, 1849, record:

Committee on portrait of Dr. Chapman. On motion of Judge Kane, a Committee of three was appointed to take measures for procuring a portrait of the late President, Dr. Chapman, to be placed in the Hall of the Society. The Committee appointed were Judge Kane, Dr. Hays, and Mr. Richards.

On May 18, 1860, it was noted:

Chapman's portrait. Bill settled. A bill was presented for the painting of a portrait of Dr. N. Chapman, by Waugh, after Sully, amounting to $125.00 and was ordered to be paid.

By Samuel Bell Waugh, *circa* 1859; the head and shoulders copied from Thomas Sully's ¾ length portrait of 1848.
Oil on Canvas. 30¼" × 25".
Painted on order; delivered 1860.
(58.P.41)

ZACCHEUS COLLINS, 1764–1831

Philanthropist, naturalist.
APS 1804; Councillor 1805–1811; Curator 1811–1819; Vice-President 1819–1831.

The catalogue of the *Twenty-third Annual Exhibition of the Pennsylvania Academy of the Fine Arts, October, 1834,* lists, p. 11, James Barton Longacre's likeness of "Zaccheus Collins, Esq. late Vice President of the American Philosophical Society, a Portrait in Sepia." The *Transactions* of the American Philosophical Society of 1834 notes under "Donations" that General Daniel Parker left at the Hall an "Original Pencil Portrait of Zaccheus Collins, late Vice-Pres. of the Society, by Longacre. This last deposited."

By James Barton Longacre, *circa* 1834.
Sepia drawing on paper. 10¼" × 8⅛".
On paper an impression of seal, worded (lower left): "SUPERFINE LONDON."
Deposited by General Daniel Parker, 1834.
(58.P.89)

MARIE JEAN ANTOINE NICOLAS CARITAT, MARQUIS DE CONDORCET, 1743–1794 (Fig. 11)

Mathematician, philosopher, statesman.
APS 1775.

Condorcet had been one of the group called "les Américains,"

15

and it had been he who had delivered the memorial eulogy on Franklin before the Académie des Sciences, November 13, 1790. The story of how, long after his death in the turmoil of the French Revolution, his portrait was brought to an honored place in Philosophical Hall is told by William Short in a letter to Thomas Jefferson, dated from Philadelphia, October 21, 1819:

Apropos of philosophers; you recollect without doubt the marble bust of Condorcet, which stood on a marble table in the salon of the Hotel de la Rochefoucauld. When it was determined no longer to receive him in that house, it was thought *inconvenient* to keep the bust there. The grandchildren, who never liked him, availed themselves of this to have the bust transported to the *garde meuble* without consulting the old lady, whose leave was generally asked on every occasion. She passed over this in silence, however, & never made a remark or enquiry as to the disappearance of the bust. It had cost her a great effort to signify to the original that his presence had become disagreeable; she had really a parental affection for him, & had given a remarkable proof of this at the time of his marriage. On her death I asked this bust of the granddaughter, who gave it to me with great pleasure. It has been on its way here ever since I left France, & has passed through as many *cases & discrimina rerum* as Eneas himself (or perhaps it was Ulysses) on its way. It has finally arrived & is at present placed in the Philosophical hall in the most suitable company, the busts of Franklin, yourself, Turgot. (Mass. His. Soc., *Collections* 1: 288–289, 1900.)

Formal presentation to the Society was made on March 19, 1830.

By Jean Antoine Houdon, 1785.
Marble bust. Height 30½".
Signed (left, below arm): "houdon / fecit / 1785."
Gift of William Short, 1830.
(58.S.2)

EDWIN GRANT CONKLIN, 1863–1952 (Fig. 52)

Biologist, university professor.

APS 1897; Secretary 1901–1908; Councillor 1915–1918, 1927–1930, 1931–1932, 1945–1948, 1952. Vice-President 1932–1942; Executive Officer 1936–1942; President 1942–1945; 1948–1952.

As a biologist, Dr. Conklin made notable contributions to the knowledge of cell lineage in embryonic development. As a professor at the University of Pennsylvania and later at Princeton, he gave to a whole generation of young men an inspiring and enlightened introduction to evolutionary theory at a time when such thinking was still controversial, even suspected, in this country. As editor of scientific journals and counsellor of nu-

16

merous scientific organizations, he exemplified through a long life the highest ideals of human learning. When he retired from his second term as President of the American Philosophical Society, the members declared in a resolution addressed to him:

... all agree that you are our indispensable member. For more than fifty-five years your identification with our Society has become more and more complete. You incarnate its philosophy, its unending search for truth and useful knowledge, its devotion to human welfare and its spiritual fellowship.

By Cameron Burnside, 1941.
Oil on canvas, 41⅛″ × 31⅛″.
Signed (lower right): "CAMERON BURNSIDE / 1941."
Painted on order, 1941.
(58.P.20)

EDWARD DRINKER COPE, 1840–1897

Zoologist, paleontologist, explorer.
APS 1866; Councillor 1885–1891.
"Only to a few men with the light of genius is it given to push the world's human thought along," and among these, in his memoir of 1930, Henry Fairfield Osborn placed Cope. The Society's portrait of Cope was described by Persifor Frazer in the *American Naturalist* of May, 1897:

The picture which occupies the frontispiece of this number was painted by Mr. George W. Pettit of Philadelphia as a labor of love, and the study of the head of a remarkable man. Without at all compromising its accuracy as a portrait, Mr. Pettit has succeeded in imparting to it a great deal of the intellectual force which was familiar to all those who knew Prof. Cope intimately. As a representation of a man it illustrates the advantage which a faithful painting has over a photograph. The latter is an accurate reproduction of the object as it was at a given minute. All appearances have equal value during this short time; the accidental and transitory as well as the permanent and characteristic. Indeed some of the latter may and usually are masked by the former and possess less than their true significance in the resulting image. On the other hand the portrait by an artist is a composite of a great number of pictures preserved in his memory, in which the salient characteristics survive and the transient and adventitious expressions disappear.

This is well illustrated by the present portrait which was begun ten years ago or more, and has been so gradually evolved that it may be said to embody the essence of the original's aspect during that period. The beard is shown as it was worn during the greater part of the subject's life, and as most of his friends will remember it. During the last two years he had dispensed with it entirely as is manifest from

17

the picture which has accompanied the greater number of the sketches of his life in newspapers and journals. This picture while pleasing in its expression, enforces what has been said of the advantage which a portrait study by an artist has over the most agreeable photograph. The intellectual expression implying alertness and activity which is so manifest in the painting (as it was in the face of Prof. Cope himself) is in this photograph subordinated to a general expression of content and repose of all the faculties. The painting has been purchased for the American Philosophical Society, and will be added to those of the distinguished men who adorn its halls.

It should be added in justice to Mr. Pettit, that since the photograph was taken from which our illustration was made, he has improved the original work very notably, thanks to the suggestions of the relatives and personal friends who have reviewed the painting, and to the inspiration due to his realizing the importance of his task. The late Russel Smith has also painted a portrait of Professor Cope which it is understood has been presented to the Academy of Natural Sciences.

By George W. Pettit, *circa* 1887–1897.
Oil on canvas. 30″ × 25″.
Signed (lower right): "G. W. Pettit 1897."
Gift of a number of members, 1897.
(58.P.56)

NICOLAS COPERNICUS, 1473–1543

Astronomer.

For the artist's own account and estimate of this small portrait, see Buchan, *above*. The errors in the Latin inscription may have been intended to add to the archaic character of the piece.

By the Earl of Buchan, after Thomas Parke's drawing after the Lorman copy at the Royal Society, London.
Water color on paper or vellum. 4″ × 37/8″.
Inscribed: "R. D. NICOLO COPERNICO / HANC EFFIGEM VERAM NICOLAI COPERNICI, / D. S. BUCHANIÆ CAMES POSTERITATI PINXIT, / AD CÆNOBIUM DE DRIBURGH IN SCOTIA."
Gift of the Earl of Buchan, 1795.
(58.P.83)

JOSÉ FRANCESCO CORREA DA SERRA, 1750–1823 (Fig. 34)

Botanist, diplomat.
APS 1812.

The election to the Society of the learned abbé, a former Secretary of Lisbon's Royal Academy of Science, followed his arrival in Philadelphia with a letter of introduction from

18

François André Michaux to John Vaughan, dated December 5, 1811. From 1816 to 1820, he served as Portuguese Minister to the United States. Of him John Quincy Adams wrote in 1818:

The Abbé Correa is a man of extensive and general literature, of profound science, of brilliant wit, and of inexhaustible powers of conversation. . . . He is insinuating and fascinating in his manner and deportment, and though sixty-eight years of age, as lively as if he were twenty-five. . . . The Abbé's diplomatic ability consists principally in affecting to be anything but a diplomat. He introduces himself as a familiar acquaintance, to talk literature and philosophy, as a domestic inmate, to gossip over a cup of tea. . . . Mr. Madison and Mr. Jefferson always received and encouraged the Abbé's social visits, and I have always done the same, always avoiding any distinction between him and any others of the foreign Ministers. (*Trans. Amer. Philos. Soc.* 45(2): 106–107, 1955.)

After Correa's return to Europe in 1820 he continued to serve as a channel of communication for scientific observation in the two hemispheres. His portrait, which had been exhibited at the Pennsylvania Academy of the Fine Arts in 1816, was received by the Society with the following letter from Joseph Hopkinson, President of the Academy, dated January 20, 1831:

I have the pleasure of informing you that at a meeting of the Directors of the "Pennsylvania Academy of the Fine Arts" it was Resolved to present to the "American Philosophical Society" a fine portrait and excellent likeness of the late *Abbé Correa,* a distinguished member of the Society, and celebrated in the learned world for his genius and acquirements. The Directors of the Academy have ordered me to make this communication to you.

By Charles B. Lawrence, *circa* 1816.
Oil on canvas. 28⅞″ × 23⅞″.
Gift of the Pennsylvania Academy of the Fine Arts, 1831.
(58.P.46)

GEORGES LÉOPOLD CHRÉTIEN FRÉDÉRIC DAGOBERT, BARON CUVIER, 1769–1832

Naturalist, comparative anatomist, educator.

The energy and universal interests of Georges Cuvier, as he preferred to be called, brought him into association with the American naturalists. In 1808 he wrote that the fossil bones sent to France by Jefferson were thought "un présent bien précieux," and that results of value were coming from foreign work, "principalement dans celui de M. Peale." When, years later, a group of French associates appealed to the world of learning for funds with which to honor Cuvier's vast accomplishment, the Society

19

responded by appointing a committee to support the project. The proposal was for a statue to be erected in the Jardin des Plantes at Paris. Dr. Chapman reported for the "Cuvier Statue Committee" on January 4, 1832, that one thousand francs had been raised. President Du Ponceau on January 5, 1833 wrote to the Secretary of the Académie des Sciences with the Society's endorsement and support:

L'objet de cette circulaire était en engageant les Savans Etrangers à contribuer à l'erection de ce noble monument, de proclamer, ainsi que le Comité s'exprime, d'une manière éclatante la confraternité des Savans & des hommes de lettres de tous les pays. Cet objet, Monsieur, est en effet digne et de ceux qui en ont conçu l'idée, et du grand homme, à la memoire duquel le monument est destiné, dont la perte est regrettée non seulement par la patrie, mais par l'univers, à qui il appartenait.

To the warm and immediate response returned to the Society from Paris was added, soon after, by the artist, a cast of his study for the memorial. In the *Transactions* of 1834 it is recorded that "M. David, Member of the Institute of France, presented to the Amer. Philosophical Society, Colossal Bust of Cuvier, inscribed 'À le Memoire de Georges Cuvier, P. J. David.' This Bust was not made for sale." The likeness had been made from a death mask by Emanuel Rousseau and from a study by David who had been an intimate friend of Cuvier. It had been passed upon by other friends and pronounced successful.

By Pierre Jean David d'Angers, *circa* 1833. Study for a marble at the Jardin des Plantes, Paris, erected by international subscription. Colossal plaster head. Height 30½".
Cast in base (right): "à la mémoire de / Georges Cuvier / P. J. David d'angers / 1833."
Gift of the artist, 1834.
(58.S.32)

CHARLES ROBERT DARWIN, 1809–1882

Naturalist, proponent of the theory of natural selection.
APS 1869
The Wedgwood bas-relief of Darwin, which is recorded as representing him also at his old college rooms at Cambridge, was the work of Thomas Woolner, monumental and portrait sculptor of the Victorian era. Among Woolner's other subjects were Dickens, Tennyson, Kingsley, Gladstone, and Cardinal Newman. He was a prominent member of the Pre-Raphaelite group. Discouraged in part by the poor reception of his medallion por-

20

trait of Thomas Carlyle, he left England for a few years in 1852, his departure memorialized by Ford Madox-Brown's famous painting, *The Last of England.* This work belongs to the successful career which followed his return.

By Wedgwood, *circa* 1905. Modeled by A. H. Bentley after the bas-relief by Thomas Woolner.
Ceramic plaque. White on green jasper dip. $12\frac{1}{16}'' \times 8\frac{1}{2}''$.
Signed on tranche of shoulder: "T. WOOLNER SC." Impressed on back: "WEDGWOOD / o."
Provenance unknown.
(58.S.45)

ERASMUS DARWIN, 1731–1802

Naturalist, physician, poet.
APS 1792.

Erasmus Darwin was physician at Lichfield, England, later at Derby; naturalist, author of poetical treatises on scientific and philosophical subjects (*The Botanic Garden, The Temple of Nature or the Origin of Society*); grandfather of Charles Darwin and Francis Galton.

By Wedgwood. Nineteenth century from late eighteenth-century model. After the painting by Joseph Wright of Derby. Modeled probably by Joseph Hackwood.
Ceramic medallion. White on blue jasper dip. $8'' \times 6''$ (oval).
Impressed on back: "WEDGWOOD" and "Dr. Darwin."
Gift of Sir George Darwin, 1906.
(58.S.54)

JEAN BAPTISTE JOSEPH DELAMBRE, 1749–1822

Astronomer.
APS 1803.

Andrew Ellicott wrote to Robert Patterson from Lancaster, January 17, 1803:

If Mr. Delambre is not already a member of our Philosophical Society, it is time he was one. I wish my name entered as one of the proposers, and trust that you will second it. If he should be elected, of which I presume there can be but little doubt, I have a desire to forward his Diploma. The nomination must be as follows (Viz) Jean Baptiste Joseph de Lambre one of the secretaries of the National Institute.

Three years later, June 10, 1806, Ellicott forwarded to John Vaughan "the first volume of the measure of the Meridian of France. It is a present from Mr. Delambre to our Philosophical Society."

21

Delambre's was one of the portraits of French savants painted from life by Rembrandt Peale for his father's Philadelphia Museum between 1808 and 1810. It is listed as No. 129 in the *Historical Catalogue of the Paintings in The Philadelphia Museum,* 1813, where the subject is describd as "one of the perpetual secretaries of the Institute of France, treasurer of the Imperial University, &c. This amiable astronomer is at the head of the observatory at Paris." The Peale gallery was dispersed at auction in 1854.

By Rembrandt Peale, *circa* 1808–1810.
Oil on canvas. $28\frac{3}{4}'' \times 23\frac{1}{4}''$.
Gift of Joseph Harrison, 1872.
(58.P.34)

FRANCIS XAVIER DERCUM, 1856–1931

Physician, teacher, medical writer.
APS 1892; Vice-President 1925–1927; President 1927–1931.

The breadth and modernity of Dr. Dercum's professional outlook was reflected again in his presidency of the Society. A letter of November 17, 1928, to Henry Fairfield Osborn reveals his eagerness to expand its activities and in particular its publications, "making it more and more useful." His life closed in this effort, dramatically, as is described in his obituary by Albert P. Brubaker:

Death came suddenly to him seated in Benjamin Franklin's chair, as he presided over the first session of the General Meeting of the Society for 1931. Surrounded by many of his scientific colleagues and friends and the portraits of many of America's great men who had bequeathed this Society to successive generations, he had just spoken concerning the progress and ambitions which the Society entertains and expressed the belief that these ambitions had every prospect of being realized. It seemed to be his bequest to the present generation. His memory will be gratefully and affectionately cherished. (*Proc. Amer. Philos. Soc.* 71: 47–48, 1932.)

By George Gibbs, from a photograph, 1934.
Oil on canvas. $40'' \times 32\frac{3}{16}''$.
Painted on order, 1933–1934.
(58.P.21)

SIMEON DeWITT, 1756–1834 (Fig. 25)

Geographer, Surveyor General of New York.
APS 1787.

During the Revolution, DeWitt had been Geographer-in-Chief to General Washington. As Dr. John Kintzing Kane wrote of him, he

22

was a skillful and indefatigable officer, a faithful student in all the branches of his profession, but found time to cultivate the cognate sciences, and to gratify and improve a natural taste for the fine arts. He took a vivid interest in every project for the diffusion of knowledge: a vigilant observer of nature himself, he was assiduous in promoting the researches of others.

On April 25, 1807, DeWitt presented to the Society a painting by Ezra Ames of the eclipse of the previous year (see p. 3), accompanying it with a written description of the phenomenon.

The portrait bust of DeWitt came to the Society from Albany as the gift of his son, Richard Varick DeWitt, the accompanying letter, dated November 18, 1839, declaring it to be "a very striking likeness of him at the age of 74."

The work was for many years listed in error as a bust of De-Witt Clinton.

By an unknown sculptor, 1830.
Plaster Bust. Height, 25".
Cut in support: "Clinton."
Gift of the Rev. Richard Varick DeWitt, 1839.
(58.S.18)

HENRY HERBERT DONALDSON, 1857–1938

Anatomist.

APS 1906; Councillor 1911–1914, 1915–1918, 1928–1931, 1932–1935; Curator 1920–1923; Vice-President 1935–1938.

Dr. Donaldson, from 1905 until his death Director of Research at the Wistar Institute of Anatomy and Biology, was a leading investigator of the nervous system. For his eightieth birthday, and the twentieth anniversary of the University of Pennsylvania's Lenape Club, Robert Tait McKenzie made this bas-relief medallion, of which the doctor-sculptor said:

I had been attracted by his distinguished and sensitive profile and the shock of wavy hair that crowned it like a nimbus, and had even suggested sittings. A community of interests brought us much together. He was interested in the effects of exercise on the muscular system, and on the weight of organs in rats he worked on in his squirrel cages, and we had many consultations and discussions on these and kindred questions. The results of his long series of patient experiments have raised the level of the great reservoir of knowledge on this important physiological question. (*Bios* 10: 18, 1939.)

By Robert Tait McKenzie, 1937.
Bronze bas-relief. Diameter, 9⅞".
Signed and inscribed: "RTM [monogram] 1937 / HENRY H. DONALDSON NEUROLOGIST PRESIDENT. LENAPE CLUB."
Purchased 1937.
(58.S.39)

23

THOMAS DUNLAP, 1792–1864

Lawyer, banker.

APS 1837.

Thomas Dunlap was the fourth and last President of the Second Bank of the United States.

Attributed to Alice De Haven, after a photograph or daguerreotype. Pastel on paper. 24″ × 20″.
Presented by estate of subject's daughter, Mrs. N. D. Conarroe, 1921. (58.P.66)

PETER STEPHEN DU PONCEAU [1], 1760–1844 (Fig. 26)

Lawyer, philologist.

APS 1791; Councillor 1801–1816; Vice-President 1816–1828; President 1828–1844.

Coming to America from France as aide-de-camp and secretary to Major General the Baron de Steuben, Du Ponceau saw active service in the Revolution, and remained to become one of our first international lawyers, and internationally noted as an authority on linguistics. He encouraged American lawyers to interest themselves in international law, and especially the doctrine of neutrality. He advocated closer cultural relations with the South American republics, hoped that the Society could be a stimulating and unifying force in those areas where, as he wrote to John Vaughan in 1832, "There are no learned Societies . . . I have laid a plan . . . to make our *American* Philosophical Society, the *center* of a scientific communication between the new world and the old."

At the time of his death Du Ponceau was President of the Society, of the Historical Society of Pennsylvania, and of the Athenaeum of Philadelphia. He held membership in twenty-three American and nineteen foreign learned societies. His philological studies, principally those on American Indian, Berber, and Chinese languages, and his *Chinese System of Writing* of 1838 had aroused world-wide interest and controversy. In a long codicil to his will, written movingly and from a full heart, he left the greater part of his library to the American Philosophical Society with the advice to that body that they "have only to pursue their present honourable course."

Du Ponceau's portrait, painted on order by Sully, is variously recorded as a gift of members and as a "Subscription of some of the Members."

24

By Thomas Sully, 1830.
Oil on canvas. 30″ × 25″.
Gift of members: Nicholas Biddle, Zaccheus Collins, George Pollock,
William Strickland, John Vaughan, 1830.
(58.P.33)

PETER STEPHEN DU PONCEAU [2]

By Fiorelli.
Marble bust. Height, 18½″.
Gift of several members by subscription, 1834.
(58.S.25)

GUGLIELMO FERRERO, 1871–1942

Italian sociologist and historian.

A vigorous writer and polemicist, passionate believer in democracy, and great admirer of the United States and the republican form of government. The plaque honors the completion and translation into English of his most important work, *Grandezza e Decadenza di Roma*, in five volumes, published in Italian in 1902–1907 and in English in 1909.

By Robert Tait McKenzie, 1909.
Plaster medallion bas-relief. Diameter 9½″.
Signed (lower edge): "R. Tait McKenzie, 1909." Inscribed: "GUGLIELMO FERRERO STORICO DI ROMA."
Provenance unknown.
(58.S.53)

FREDERICK FRALEY, 1804–1901 (Fig. 44)

Merchant, banker.

APS 1842; Councillor 1851–1857 and 1861–1872; Secretary 1853–1859; Vice-President 1869–1880; President 1880–1901.

The Minutes of April 15, 1898, record that

A letter was received from Mr. Rosengarten, on behalf of a number of subscribers, donating portraits of the Hon. Frederick Fraley and Prof. J. Peter Lesley, both painted by Mrs. Margaret Lesley Bush-Brown, and requesting the Society to arrange for their formal presentation. . . .

On motion it was resolved that the best thanks of the Society be presented through Mr. Rosengarten to the donors of the portraits of the Hon. Frederick Fraley and Prof. J. Peter Lesley, and that Friday evening, May 20th. be assigned for their formal presentation and acceptance.

On that evening, in presenting the portrait of Fraley, Albert H. Smyth said:

25

It had been the intention and the hope of Mr. J. G. Rosengarten to be present this evening and in accordance with the request of the subscribers, to present to the American Philosophical Society two portraits, one of Mr. Frederick Fraley, our honored President, the other of Prof. John [sic] Peter Lesley, for many years a Vice-President of this Society.

A little while ago several of the friends of Mr. Fraley within and without this Society, desiring to express, as Hamlet says, their "love and friending" to him, and to place in the Hall of the Society over which he has presided with such zeal and success some token of their admiration and respect, learned that an excellent portrait of him had been painted.

To this Hampton L. Carson added:

It is fitting that his portrait should grace these walls—walls hallowed by sacred associations and cherished with filial piety. "I would rather," said Hazlitt, "leave behind me a good portrait than a good epitaph." The sentiment is just. Those who read tombstone inscriptions are few, but those who can find inspiration in the study of a well-pictured face are many. This Society, grateful to the donors of this admirable portrait, will direct it to be hung beside those of the illustrious men who were his predecessors, in commemoration of the virtues, the talents and the services of Frederick Fraley.

By Margaret Lesley Bush-Brown, *circa* 1898.
Oil on canvas. $36\frac{1}{16}'' \times 30''$.

(58.P.57)

Members and friends, donors of the portraits of Frederick Fraley and J. Peter Lesley, were: Alexander Biddle, Maria Blanchard, James C. Brooks, Clarence H. Clark, Samuel Dickson, George F. Edmunds, W. W. Frazier, A. T. Freedley, John B. Gest, J. E. Gillingham, Lincoln Godfrey, C. A. Griscom, Alfred C. Harrison, Charles C. Harrison, Charles Hartshorne, Herbert M. Howe, Helen C. Jenks, John S. Jenks, William V. McKean, John V. Merrick, Matthew H. Meschers, Henry N. Paul, John W. Paul, Jr., Robert Patterson, Fanny Rosengarten, Joseph G. Rosengarten, Coleman Sellers, N. Parker Shortridge, William P. Tatham, George C. Thomas, Frank Thomson, James P. Townsend, John Wanamaker, Charles Wharton, W. A. Winsor, Charles S. Wurtz, 1898.

BENJAMIN FRANKLIN, 1706–1790

Printer, journalist, scientist, diplomat, statesman.

APS Founder 1743; Secretary 1743; President 1769–1790.

"Your father's face," Franklin wrote from France to his daughters on June 3, 1779, is "as well known as that of the moon, so that he durst not do anything that would oblige him to run away,

26

as his phiz would discover him wherever he should venture to show it." The Society possesses a fair representation of those multitudinous and varying reflections of his "phiz" which Franklin was describing, important parts of it catalogued elsewhere. In the Library's Peale-Sellers Collection there is a small pencil sketch of 1767 which may depict Franklin, and certainly shows its subject in an informal pose in which young Charles Willson Peale had seen Franklin at that time. The Bache Collection contains a little pen-and-ink profile drawing of *circa* 1794, showing how Franklin stood in the recollection of his grandson, Benjamin Franklin Bache. The Print Collection is rich in Frankliniana, much of it of importance as portraiture and all of it important in the documentation of his life.

Paintings:

BENJAMIN FRANKLIN [1] (Fig. 1)

Of the formal likenesses owned by the Society that which has reflected him here over the longest period, with complete fidelity and with a wholly appropriate charm, is the copy of David Martin's portrait of 1767, painted in 1772 by Charles Willson Peale, probably with his brother James sharing in the work. On December 16, 1785, Peale presented this picture to the Society apparently as his contribution to the recently launched project for the erection of Philosophical Hall—stating his great respect for the Society and his opinion that every man must naturally "express his Sensibility in that manner which accords best with his own Habits & Line of business." The members in returning their thanks asked him to retain it "till the Society shall have a convenient Place for its reception."

At the meeting of July 19, 1789, from which Peale was absent, discussion of Franklin's failing health led to a resolution that Peale paint a new portrait to be hung in the then nearly completed building. This the artist did, painting the half-length now owned by the Historical Society of Pennsylvania. He then allowed his confreres, who had passed their resolution forgetful of his earlier gift, to choose between the two. Their selection of the copy after Martin has never been regretted. After removal to the Hall, December 2, 1791, a new frame was ordered for the painting, this transaction being completed February 3 and 17, 1792, with the payment of James Reynolds' bill. In 1814 Thomas Birch repaired the picture at a charge of $14.00. In 1843 it was cleaned, relined, and reframed by Earle at a price of $16.00.

In the original portrait painted in London by Martin, Franklin is shown seated in a chair with an ornately carved and gilded back. It would appear that Franklin, in ordering a replica for himself, specified a much simpler piece of furniture, a change which reinforced the strength and character of the work. Peale's copy is from that replica.

By Charles Willson Peale (and perhaps also James Peale), copy after David Martin's portrait of 1767, 1772.
Oil on canvas. 49″ × 38½″.
Gift of Charles Willson Peale, 1785.
(58.P.1)

BENJAMIN FRANKLIN [2] (Fig. 2)

The painting attributed to Charles Van Loo stands unique and authentic in Franklin portraiture, a life portrait of superb warmth and intimacy, painted for the home of a beloved friend. It has a continuous history until its acquisition by the Society as in the possession first of Madame Helvétius and then in the family of her daughter, the Marquise de Mun. "It is a Franklin," as Gilbert Chinard described it in the Society's *Proceedings* of 1950, "benevolent, smiling, and amused, with a twinkle in his eye, completely relaxed and ready to talk. This is indeed 'bon papa Franklin,'" the grandfatherly Franklin so much at home in the Château de Lumigny with the mother and the two daughters whom he called the "little stars." It was Dr. Chinard who discovered the portrait in Paris and brought it to Philadelphia.

The date of the picture, made for a private friend and not at the time of its completion either exhibited or engraved, is unknown, but must belong to the early ripening of the friendship between its subject and its first owner. The earliest record of it is in Jean Baptiste Le Roy's "Notes" to Abbé Fauchet's *Eulogy* of 1790:

Sa meilleure amie, celle chez qui il se livroit le plus volontiers à une conversation libre et amusante et où il aimoit à passer le tems que lui laissoient les affaires, la Vᵉ d'Helvétius le faisoit peindre chez elle. "Amusez moi, disoit-il à ses amis, ou vous aurez de moi le plus triste des portraits." (*Proc. Amer. Philos. Soc.* **94:** 219, 1950.)

Attributed to Charles Amedée Philippe Van Loo.
Oil on canvas. 28½″ × 22⅞″ (oval).
Purchased 1948.
(58.P.2)

BENJAMIN FRANKLIN [3]

The earliest of the many French portraits of Franklin was a drawing by Charles Nicolas Cochin. An engraving from it by Augustin de Saint Aubin was published in July, 1777. The

28

Doctor is shown wearing his spectacles and the famous Canadian fur cap at what was perhaps the most dramatic moment of his career. Through hostile ships and winter storms he had come to the courts and people of Europe to plead the cause of American liberty. The Cochin likeness enjoyed an enormous popularity and innumerable repetitions of it were made. The Society's portrait, discovered in Germany at the close of World War II, had descended in the Wille family, some of whose forebears had been engravers associated with the French school of the eighteenth century. Among portrait engravers it was a common practice to paint the name of its subject on a canvas to be used as a source, in order to avoid errors, as appears in this example.

By an unidentified painter, after Charles Nicolas Cochin's drawing or the engraving from it by Augustin de Saint Aubin, *circa* 1777–1780.
Oil on canvas. 22½″ × 18¾″.
Inscribed (lower left): "Franklin."
Purchased 1951.
(58.P.62)

BENJAMIN FRANKLIN [4]

The most famous and the most frequently copied of all Franklin portraits is the "Fur Collar" painting of 1778 by Joseph Siffred Duplessis, the original of which is now at the Metropolitan Museum. Copies made from other copies are inevitably imperfect reflections of the original, and yet do reflect the spread of Franklin's fame and the eagerness everywhere for memorials of it. The Society's oil portrait after Duplessis is of this character. It may have been taken from a copy said to have been owned by the Pennsylvania Hospital *circa* 1850 but now unlocated, or it may have been made from Thomas B. Welch's copy of that picture made for the City of Philadelphia in 1855.

By an unidentified artist, after a Duplessis-type portrait.
Oil on canvas. 30″ × 25″.
Provenance unknown.
(58.P.70)

BENJAMIN FRANKLIN [5]. Franklin Urging the Claims of the American Colonies before Louis XVI (Fig. 56)

Toward the end of his stormy reign, *circa* 1846–1847, King Louis Philippe commissioned for Versailles a monumental historical painting, with life-size figures, depicting Franklin's appeal to France for the cause of American liberty. Also to adorn his palace he ordered at the same time and from the same artist a

29

group of portraits of the leading contemporary American states-men. The choice of artist was singularly appropriate. George Peter Alexander Healy had come to Paris from Boston in 1834 to study art, and had remained to become one of the most force-ful and popular portrait painters among the elite of that and other European capitals, through all of which he had remained a blunt, firm exponent of American democracy and America's expanding future.

The great painting, of which the Society owns the original study, was completed as a private undertaking after the abdica-tion of Louis Philippe in 1848. It won a medal at the Paris Universal Exposition of 1855, was brought to Chicago where Healy opened a studio in the next year, and was eventually de-stroyed in the Chicago fire of 1871. Recognizable in the Society's original version, in addition to Franklin and the King and Queen, are the Cardinal de Rohan, the Comte de Vergennes, Beaumarchais, and Franklin's fellow commissioners, Silas Deane and Arthur Lee.

By George Peter Alexander Healy, *circa* 1847.
Oil on canvas. 24″ × 36″.
Purchased 1941.
(58.P.28)

Miniatures:

BENJAMIN FRANKLIN [6]

Mason Chamberlin's portrait of Franklin painted in 1762 is represented in the Society's collection by a copy in miniature, probably dating from the early nineteenth century. A very similar (perhaps the same) miniature was in the large and dis-tinguished collection of Francis Wellesley, dispersed at auction in London in 1920.

By an unidentified artist after Mason Chamberlin's portrait of 1762.
Opaque water color on ivory. $4\,5\!/\!16''$ × $3\,5\!/\!8''$.
Purchased 1953.
(58.P.78)

BENJAMIN FRANKLIN [7]

As the painting by Van Loo [2] occupies a supreme place as an informal, private portrait, so the painting by Duplessis, the original of which is in the Metropolitan Museum in New York, stands in front rank as a formal statement. In the Society's col-lection the Duplessis is best represented by a miniature, the work of an excellent, if unknown, artist.

30

The miniature is mounted on a small leather stand, to which a seal with a wreath, stars, and monogram has been clipped from a paper and attached. Also attached is a printed label, "Vu & certifié véritable par / nous Membres du Jury des Arts" with the signatures "Mellot J. Minot. C. Guillemes." No actual relationship between the miniature and the attached papers has been established.

By an unidentified artist, *circa* 1780–1805, after the painting by Joseph Siffred Duplessis, 1778.
Water color on ivory. $1\frac{3}{4}'' \times 1\frac{7}{8}''$ (oval).
Purchased 1956.
(58.P.76)

BENJAMIN FRANKLIN [8]

A second miniature after Duplessis in the Society's collection is based not upon the "fur collar" version, but upon the pastel owned by Franklin himself and now in the New York Public Library. In order to avoid the tedium of posing, Franklin repeatedly urged the painters who came to him hoping for a life portrait to copy this work instead. Some, in doing so, made use of their brief observation of the subject to vary the likeness. It is possible that this miniature may be in that class.

By an unidentified artist, *circa* 1780–1805, after the pastel by Joseph Siffred Duplessis, 1778.
Water color on ivory. $1\frac{3}{4}'' \times 1\frac{7}{16}''$ (oval).
Purchased 1952.
(58.P.77)

BENJAMIN FRANKLIN [9]

A miniature, formerly in the collection of Arthur Bloch of Philadelphia, was listed as No. 182 in the Bloch sale, 1954, and there attributed to "Copé."

Attributed to Margaretta P. Cope, after a Duplessis-type likeness.
Water color on ivory. $3\frac{3}{8}'' \times 2\frac{5}{8}''$.
Signed (lower right): "Cope."
Purchased 1957.
(58.P.80)

Drawings:

BENJAMIN FRANKLIN [10]

Though its frequent attribution to Benjamin West must be questioned, the Society's portrait drawing of Franklin after the Caffiéri bust, framed in wood from the floor of Independence

31

Hall, is one of the most attractive as well as one of the best-known treasures in its collection. It comes from West's collection, bears his autograph on the reverse, and may have been acquired by him when, after the winning of independence, he was gathering material on Franklin's likeness for use in a series of historical paintings which would record and celebrate the event. The drawing was subsequently owned by the Hon. Samuel W. Pennypacker, who first attributed it to West, and by John Wanamaker.

By an unidentified artist, *circa* 1790, after a Caffiéri-type bust.
Pencil on paper. 8¾" × 7¼" (oval).
Inscribed on reverse: "A Portrait of Benjamin Franklin / Benjn. West."
Purchased 1938.
(58.P.81)

BENJAMIN FRANKLIN [11]

This powerful drawing appears to be based upon an unlocated Houdon bust in which Franklin is shown with classic drapery upon the shoulders rather than plain contemporary dress. Such a piece is seen in the background of the painting of Houdon's studio by Louis Léopold Boilly, 1804.

By Jean Jacques François Lebarbier, l'Aîné.
Chalk on tinted paper. 20" × 15⅜".
Signed at base of oval: "Le Barbier L'Aine depres [*sic*] Le Buste de houdon [*sic*]."
Deposited by the Metropolitan Museum of Art (Huntington Collection), New York, 1958.
(58.P.79)

Sculpture: Life-size:

BENJAMIN FRANKLIN [12]

Probably the most exact and authoritative of all the Franklin portraits is the bust made by Jean Jacques Caffiéri in 1777, from life, and exhibited at the Salon in Paris in that year.

A document in the Society's Franklin Papers, hitherto unpublished and unidentified, fixes for the first time the approximate date of the completion of the Caffieri portrait. It is a note from the artist to his subject:

M. Caffieri a l honneur de soiter [*sic*] le bon jour a Monsieur franklin et le pris de lui faire dire quel jour il voudra bien lui donné, pour la derniere séance de Paris ce 26 mars 1777.

The sculptor made numerous casts from this work, including several ordered by Franklin as gifts to friends. One of these

32

came into the possession of the Pennsylvania Hospital during his lifetime. At the building of Library Hall (1789–1790) the Library Company left a niche on the second-floor level of the façade, in which a statue of its founder might be placed. William Bingham offered to donate the statue. Toward this purpose the Hospital's bust and a sketch to show the proportions of the body were sent to Italy. Franklin himself had been consulted on the matter, and was reported to favor "a Gown for his dress and a Roman Head." In 1792 there was returned to Philadelphia a larger-than-life marble statue, the work of a little-known Cararese sculptor, Francesco Lazzarini, who had appropriately introduced into the composition a pile of books upon which one arm rested, and a sceptre, inverted, as a symbol of anti-monarchical principles. The statue was one of the sights of Philadelphia until its removal, much damaged by the weather, August 25, 1879. The old Library Hall was razed in 1887.

The plans for the Society's new library building included an identical niche and in it an identical statue, bringing back to "the minds of his fellow citizens," as the Library Company's minutes of 1792 had recorded, "a recollection of the public and private Virtues of its Original."

By Lewis Iselin, Jr., 1958–1959, after Francesco Lazzarini and Jean Jacques Caffiéri.
Marble statue. Height 98".
Inscribed on base: "B. FRANKLIN / REPLICA OF THE STATUE BY LAZZARINI / PRESENTED TO THE LIBRARY COMPANY 1792 / BY WILLIAM BINGHAM."
On commission, 1958.
(59.S.1)

BENJAMIN FRANKLIN [13] (Fig. 3)

The shipment of a Caffiéri bust of Franklin to Italy for use in making the statue described above gave Italian sculptors an important model to work from. It was very probably the source of the marble bust presented to the Society on July 20, 1804, by John Rhea Smith. In his letter of presentation the donor stated that, "It is of Italian workmanship, executed at Florence, & from my imperfect recollection of the Doctor's features, would seem to be a good likeness."

By an unidentified Italian sculptor, circa 1800, after Jean Jacques Caffiéri.
Marble bust. Height 27¼".
Gift of John Rhea Smith, 1804.
(58.S.1)

33

BENJAMIN FRANKLIN [14]

The Society's plaster cast after Caffiéri may have come from the studio of George M. Miller, a Philadelphia sculptor, and may have the same provenance as the bust of William White ($q.v.$). A very similar bust owned by the Library Company was given to it by Walter Franklin, January 17, 1805. The Society's only record accompanying its example is that it was used by the United States Government for the "penny postage stamp."

By an unidentified artist, after Jean Jacques Caffiéri.
Plaster bust. Height 28⅝".
Provenance unknown.
(58.S.29)

BENJAMIN FRANKLIN [15] (Fig. 4)

The busts of Franklin by Caffiéri, 1777, and by Jean Antoine Houdon, 1778, are often seen in contrast, the first a powerfully accurate portrait from life, the second made not from sittings but from informal observation and so less exact, though a moving and wholly successful characterization. Houdon gave four casts of his work to Franklin, and it may have been one of these which Franklin's grand-nephew, Jonathan Williams, who had been with him in France, presented to the Society on August 15, 1800. Two years later Joseph Sansom returned from Europe bringing a plaster cast, formal presentation of which to the Society was made on January 21, 1803. Sansom's, a variant of the other, was described in the *Transactions* of 1809 as "By Flaxman after Houdon." At the meeting of February 18, 1803, it was

Resolved That in consideration of the Society's being in possession of two Casts of a Bust of Doctr. Franklin from originals by the celebrated Houdon, one of these casts, with the consent of the donor, Jonathan Williams, be sent in the name of the Society to the Academy of Arts and Sciences in Boston with a copy of his letter to the Society.

This was done, and the Williams bust still occupies a place of honor in the hall of the American Academy of Arts and Sciences, at Boston.

While the name of John Flaxman adds much interest to the piece which the Society retained, it is a somewhat softened version of Houdon's original. Hiram Powers made some copies of a similar cast in marble, slightly variant, but reflecting Flaxman's added smoothness and calm. Joseph Sansom, the donor, later

34

used the likeness in producing a series of historical medals, examples of which are in the Society's collection.

Cast of a copy after Jean Antoine Houdon's bust of 1778, by John Flaxman, 1802.
Plaster bust. Height 26½".
Gift of Joseph Sansom, 1803.
(59.S.30)

BENJAMIN FRANKLIN [16]

The Minutes for January 2, 1863, carried:

Dr. Wood, the president, presented to the Society a marble bust of Franklin, on a tall cylindrical pedestal of dark scagliola. Dr. Wood gave the order to an artist of Florence M. Manconi [sic] to execute this life size reduction in marble of a gigantic plaster bust of Franklin in the private collection of Mr. Packinham (a banker in Rome) at his residence in Florence. Mr. Powers the American sculptor had himself executed a copy of this bust for his own studio. Dr. Wood had the same artist to copy, life size, a gigantic plaster bust of Washington, in the same Collection. Both of plaster busts are ascribed to Houdon.

On motion of Prof. Cresson, the thanks of the Society were presented to Dr. Wood, for his munificent donation.

By Domenico Menconi after Jean Antoine Houdon.
Marble bust. Height 29½".
Signed: "Menconi / f[ecit]."
(58.S.24)

Sculpture: Small:

BENJAMIN FRANKLIN [17]

Perhaps the most authoritative of the few full-length representations of Franklin is the posthumous sculpture first exhibited at the Paris Salon of 1793. It was catalogued as No. 62, "Francklin en pied. Terre cuit, de 14 pouces de proportion. Par Suzanne." Examples of the original terra cotta by François Marie Suzanne are owned by the Metropolitan Museum of art and by the Walters Art Gallery. It has certainly been the most popular and the most frequently copied of all the Franklin statuettes.

By an unidentified French sculptor of the nineteenth century, after the terra cotta of 1793 by François Marie Suzanne.
Bronze figure. Height 5", on wooden base, 4⅝".
Purchased 1958.
(58.S.64)

35

BENJAMIN FRANKLIN [18]

By an unidentified French sculptor of the nineteenth century, after
the Suzanne figure or a copy of it.
Brass figure. Height $8\frac{7}{8}''$, on wooden base, $2\frac{3}{8}''$.
Purchased 1958.
(58.S.65)

BENJAMIN FRANKLIN [19]

By an unidentified French sculptor of the nineteenth century, after
the head and shoulders of the Suzanne figure, or a copy of it.
White metal bust, $4\frac{5}{16}''$, on brass base, $2\frac{7}{8}''$.
Purchased 1956.
(58.S.66)

BENJAMIN FRANKLIN [20]

Staffordshire pottery, after a copy of the Suzanne figure.
China figure. Height $14''$.
Inscribed on base: "General Washington."
Purchased 1953.
(58.S.67)

BENJAMIN FRANKLIN [21]

Staffordshire pottery, suggested by the Suzanne figure.
China figure. Height $7\frac{1}{2}''$.
Inscribed on base: "FRANKLIN."
Purchased 1958.
(58.S.68)

BENJAMIN FRANKLIN [22]

The small seated figure of Franklin, apparently a free adap-
tation in a new pose of the likeness in the Suzanne statuette, is
the work of an eminent French sculptor who had been a student of David d'Angers (creator of the Society's heroic head of
Georges Cuvier) and who became director of art work at Sèvres.

By Albert Ernest Carrier-Belleuse, *circa* 1870–1880.
Bronze figure. Height $10\frac{1}{4}''$.
Signed on base: "Carrier sc." Inscribed on book in pocket: "Science"
and on side of tree stump: "ERIPUIT COELO / FULMEN
SCEP / TRUMQUE / TYRANIS."
Purchased 1955.
(58.S.69)

BENJAMIN FRANKLIN [23]

Many of the later portraits of Franklin, in sculpture especially,
reflect national attitudes and trends more clearly than their

36

subject. In the Society's large bronze statuette the features are softened and idealized, the figure stands, lightning rod in hand, in an attitude of gentle acquiescence totally foreign to the "Poor Richard" of fact and of earlier portraiture, while book and static electricity machine are set upon a pedestal more suggestive of the altar of a faith than of a laboratory table. In the inscription there is no reference to the Tyrant, an allusion which might have been considered officially inappropriate in mid-nineteenth century France.

By an unidentified French sculptor, nineteenth century.
Bronze figure. Height $19\frac{3}{4}''$ on wooden base, $2\frac{1}{4}''$.
Inscribed on scroll beside book and electrical machine: "Ravit / aux Cieux / la Foundre."
Purchased 1953.
(58.S.70)

BENJAMIN FRANKLIN [24]

Small models of the philosopher in action in his laboratory or study were popular from late eighteenth to mid-nineteenth century. The observer must determine for himself whether the Society's shows Franklin, pen in hand, as an author, or whether he holds his lightning rod and is contemplating some new improvement in it.

By unidentified artist, nineteenth century.
White metal figure, with white metal and glass accessories on wooden base.
Height 14".
Books under the chair inscribed: "PHYSIQUE," "CHIMIE / 1700" and "ECONOMI."
Books at feet inscribed: "PROVERBES" and "LA / SCIENCE / DU / Bonhomme / Richard."
Purchased 1954.
(58.S.71)

BENJAMIN FRANKLIN [25]

By an unidentified artist, after the Cochin engraving. Date unknown.
Carved ivory, perhaps as a handle for cane or umbrella. Height $5\frac{3}{16}''$, on wooden base, $2\frac{1}{4}''$.
Inscribed: "Benjamin / Franklin / 1778."
Purchased 1958.
(58.S.72)

BENJAMIN FRANKLIN [26]

The Society's small statuette of cream-colored Staffordshire china honors Franklin's fame more clearly than Franklin him-

37

self. It is attributed to Ralph Wood (1716–1772) of the well-known family of craftsmen in this medium. Frank Falkner praises the piece as a portrait which "shows the lifelike expression of the American philosophe" (*Wood Family of Burslem,* 16, London, 1912). The figure stands, appropriately, with a book in its left hand and the right extended as if holding the kite string, while the face is turned upward toward the storm and the kite. A medal, presumably the Royal Society's Copley award, is hung about the neck by a ribbon. The fur-lined robe hanging from the left shoulder to the feet may be taken as indicative of Franklin's honorary academic degrees.

Intruding upon this effective combination is the fact that the figure's costume is that of a Continental gentleman of the early years of the eighteenth century and that this links it inescapably to the German factories where the art of pottery sculpture had recently originated and which, by import and imitation, were having a profound effect upon the growth of the industry in England. The facts are lost in the confused and shadowy history of the craft, but unconvincing likeness and alien costume together suggest that the English potter took the elements of an imported figure and perhaps somewhat rearranged them to honor the famous American. The same figure with a different pose of the head is recorded. The Metropolitan Museum of Art owns an identical piece, but in color, the robe trimmed with ermine, and "Dr. Franklin" inscribed on the pedestal. Similar pedestals are used in Ralph Wood's "Gamekeeper" and other figures attributed to him.

By Ralph Wood, *circa* 1762–1772, perhaps from a German mold. China figure. Height 13½".
Purchased 1958.
(58.S.73)

Medallions and Plaques:

BENJAMIN FRANKLIN [27]

An original portrait contemporary with Martin's painting of Franklin, from which the copy by Peale [1] is derived, is the small wax profile by Isaac Gosset. Gosset, a Londoner of Huguenot descent, was famous for his accuracy and quickness in this subtle and fragile art, though he earned his livelihood largely as frame-maker and business representatitive to other artists, among whom were Allan Ramsay and Ramsay's associate,

38

David Martin. The Gosset profile of Franklin was repeated in a well-known Wedgwood medallion and in other forms. It was for many years attributed to the American sculptress, Patience Wright.

Gosset undoubtedly repeated this work a number of times. The Society, however, owns the only example with a continuous history. It was given by Franklin either to his landlady, Mrs. Margaret Stevenson, or to her daughter, Mrs. Thomas Hewson, and descended in that family to its last private owner, Miss Frances M. Bradford, of Philadelphia.

By Isaac Gosset, 1766.
Wax profile. Height $3\frac{5}{16}''$.
Purchased 1960.
(60.S.1)

BENJAMIN FRANKLIN [28]

By Wedgwood, from model of *circa* 1766, after the wax bas-relief
by Isaac Gosset (see above).
Ceramic medallion. White on black jasper dip. $5\frac{5}{16}'' \times 3\frac{5}{16}''$
(oval).
Impressed on back: "Franklin" and "WEDGWOOD."
Provenance unknown.
(58.S.55)

BENJAMIN FRANKLIN [29]

From the sculptor and engraver Nini came the most popular and most frequently repeated likeness of the Doctor. His terra cotta medallions, copies and versions of them were everywhere. He was employed at the pottery and glass factory at Chaumont sur Loire, the proprietor of which was Jacques Donatien Le Ray de Chaumont, upon whose estate at Passy Franklin lived. The first and most famous of the medallions presents an intimate, homely portrait, and is frankly directed to enhancing the popularity of the American cause. The portrait was not made from life, and the fur cap is a conventionalized approximation of that which Franklin actually wore at his arrival in France.

The Society's example may be the only one extant with a continuous history to its original owner. It was brought to America by Gérard de Rayneval, first French Minister to the United States, and presented by him to Charles Willson Peale, perhaps in 1779 when Peale was painting his portrait of Gérard.

By Jean Baptiste Nini, 1777, after a drawing by Thomas Walpole, Jr.
Signed under shoulder: "NINI / F / 1777" and a device. Inscribed:
"B. FRANKLIN... AMERICAIN." Note in ink on reverse:
Presented to C. W. Peale / by mons. Gerard / French Minister
to / the United States."
Terra cotta medallion bas-relief. Diameter $4\frac{5}{8}''$.
Purchased 1950.
(58.S.74)

BENJAMIN FRANKLIN [30]

By Wedgwood, from model of *circa*, 1777–1779, based on the Nini
"Fur Cap" medallion of 1777.
Ceramic medallion. White on blue jasper dip with white self frame.
$4\frac{1}{2}'' \times 3\frac{7}{16}''$ (oval).
Inscribed on back: "BENJAMIN FRANKLIN / 1706–1790." Im-
pressed on back: "WEDGWOOD."
Provenance unknown.
(58.S.75)

BENJAMIN FRANKLIN [31]

By Wedgwood. Another version of the above.
Ceramic medallion. White on green jasper dip. $4\frac{3}{8}'' \times 3\frac{1}{8}''$ (oval).
Impressed on back: "WEDGWOOD" and "Franklin."
Provenance unknown.
(58.S.76)

BENJAMIN FRANKLIN [32]

The Nini medallion of Franklin with the fur cap was never
exceeded in popularity. Nini's later versions sought to add dig-
nity to the head and more force to the inscription. They represented not simply the philosopher pleading his country's cause,
but the Minister Plenipotentiary of a recognized nation in military alliance with France.

By Jean Baptiste Nini, 1779, possibly after a drawing by Anne Val-
layer-Coster.
Terra cotta medallion bas-relief. Diameter, $6\frac{1}{2}''$.
Signed under shoulder: "I. B. NINI F 1779." Inscribed: "B.
FRANKLIN. IL DIRIGE LA FOUDRE ET BRAVE LES
TIRANS."
Purchased 1948.
(58.S.77)

BENJAMIN FRANKLIN [33]

The famous "Classic" profile, the most freely modeled and individual of the Wedgwood Franklin medallions, is generally
believed to be the work of William Hackwood, Josiah Wedg-

40

wood's principal modeler of portraits, and to represent his interpretation of the Nini medallion of 1779.

By Wedgwood, *circa* 1905. Modeled by A. H. Bentley from model of *circa* 1780. Probably modeled by William Hackwood from the Nini medallion of 1779.
Ceramic plaque. White on green jasper dip. 12″ × 8½″.
Inscribed in relief on the field: "FRANKLIN." Impressed on back: "WEDGWOOD / o."
Gift of Sir George Darwin, 1906.
(58.S.56)

BENJAMIN FRANKLIN [34–35]

The Reception of Franklin at the Court of France.
Signing the Treaty of Paris.

These two bas-reliefs appear on the base of the statue of Franklin by John J. Boyle which was unveiled in Paris on April 27, 1906, on the occasion of the bicentennial of his birth. The titles of the scenes are on contemporary labels: *Reception de Franklin de Louis XVI / et Marie Antoinette à la Cour de France à Versailles / 1778* and *Signature de Traité de Paris / entre les Etats Unis d'Amerique & l'Angleterre /1785 [sic]*. The original models had already won an Honorable Mention at the Paris Salon of 1897, and had been exhibited there at the Exposition Universelle, 1900. An article in the Philadelphia *Ledger,* December 10, 1905, states that the "rising young French sculptor" had made the designs "under the direction of Mr. Charles Knight (son of the well-known American painter, Ridgway Knight), himself an architect, who designed the pedestal," and that both, in planning the backgrounds and accessories, had received "the kindly help of the curator of the palace of Versailles." The Boyle statue was presented to the City of Paris by John J. Harjes, resident member in Paris of Morgan, Harjes and Company, and these plaques came to the Society in the following year also as his gift.

By Frédéric Brou, 1906, after his original models of *circa* 1897.
Bronze bas-reliefs. 25½″ × 45″.
Both signed and inscribed (lower left): "Frederic Brou 1906" and "I. Hess & Fils Fondeurs."
Gift of John J. Harjes, 1907.
(58.S.36–37)

MRS. BENJAMIN FRANKLIN (DEBORAH READ), 1705–1774

At the beginning of Franklin's long residence in England he sought to lessen the pain of separation in "all our little family"

41

by having portraits painted for the London and Philadelphia homes. That of Deborah is believed to be Benjamin Wilson's copy of an American original, painted at about the same time as Wilson's well-known portrait of her husband. They are similar in style and of the same size. Franklin brought this picture back from London with him in 1775, and the two paintings were together until, in 1778, his portrait was taken by John André as a prize of war. On October 23, 1785, Franklin wrote from Philadelphia to Mme Lavoisier, who had painted and sent to him a copy of the portrait that had hung in his home at Passy:

Our English Enemies, when they were in Possession of this City and of my House, made a Prisoner of my Portrait, and carried it off with them, leaving that of its companion, my Wife, by itself, a kind of Widow. You have replaced the Husband, and the Lady seems to smile, as well pleased. (Archives Nationales, Paris.)

Attributed to Benjamin Wilson, *circa* 1758–1759, after an American portrait.
Oil on canvas. $29\frac{3}{4}'' \times 24\frac{7}{8}''$.
Purchased 1953.
(58.P.44)

WILLIAM FRANKLIN, *ca.* 1730–1813

Governor of New Jersey.
APS 1768.

The Wedgwood medallions of the loyalist governor, son of Benjamin Franklin, and of his insurgent son, William Temple Franklin (*q.v.*) are similar in proportions and design, face one another, and were apparently made at the same time and as a companion pair. This must have occurred after the treaty of peace, when the two men met again in England. That of Governor Franklin is first listed in the Wedgwood catalogue of 1787.

By Wedgwood, after the model of *circa* 1785–1787, attributed to John Flaxman.
Ceramic medallion. White on black jasper dip. $5\frac{1}{4}'' \times 3\ 15/16''$ (oval).
Impressed on back: "Govr. Franklin" and "WEDGWOOD."
Provenance unknown.
(58.S.57)

WILLIAM TEMPLE FRANKLIN, 1760–1823

Secretary to his grandfather Benjamin Franklin, and editor of his works.
APS 1786.
See above.

42

By Wedgwood, after the model of *circa* 1785–1787, variously attributed to John Flaxman and John Charles Lochee.
Ceramic medallion. White on black jasper dip. $5\frac{1}{8}'' \times 3\frac{7}{8}''$ (oval).
Impressed on back: "W. T. Franklin" and "WEDGWOOD."
Provenance unknown.
(58.S.58)

THOMAS SOVEREIGN GATES, 1873–1948 (Fig. 54)

Lawyer, financier, university administrator.
APS 1930; Vice-President 1944–1945; President 1945–1948.

Trained for the legal profession, Thomas S. Gates became a banker, serving as director or trustee of numerous financial and philanthropic organizations of local and national importance. After a career of distinguished success as a financier, he was President of the University of Pennsylvania from 1930 to 1944, leading it through a notable period of expansion and administrative reorganization.

By Alice Kent Stoddard, 1958, after her portrait of 1937.
Oil on canvas. $40\frac{1}{4}'' \times 35 \frac{3}{16}''$.
Signed (lower left): "A. K. STODDARD / COPY '58."
Gift of Mrs. Thomas Sovereign Gates, 1958.
(58.P.15)

JOHN BANNISTER GIBSON, 1780–1853

Jurist.
APS 1821.

A lawyer with widely ranging interests, John Bannister Gibson was appointed Chief Justice of the Supreme Court of Pennsylvania in 1827, on the death of William Tilghman. He had in his long term in office a profound influence on state law, his opinions and decisions noted for clarity, brevity, and mastery of the points at issue. He was an amateur musician, an amateur of the fine arts, a student of Shakespeare and of French and Italian literature. Medicine, dentistry, mechanics, entered his purview also.

A bust of Judge Gibson was exhibited at the Pennsylvania Academy of the Fine Arts, 1864 to 1870, as by Luigi Persico.

Attributed to E. Luigi Persico, *circa* 1837.
Plaster bust. Height $23\frac{1}{4}''$.
Gift of Chief Justice Gibson, 1837.
(58.S.8)

43

ALEXANDER HAMILTON [1] 1757–1804

Statesman. U. S. Secretary of the Treasury, 1789–1795.
APS 1780.

Hamilton's sudden and tragic death brought him into immediate fame as a great historic figure and as a symbol of conservative probity. His portrait was in enormous demand and to meet it, among the rest, many casts were made of the bust by the mercurial radical agitator, Giuseppe Ceracchi. Ceracchi was himself a member of the Society, as well as a close friend of David Rittenhouse, whose portrait by him is also in this collection.

Cast after a Giuseppe Ceracchi marble.
Plaster bust. Height 24″.
Cast in shoulder: "DE FACIA PHILADELPHIA, EX ECTIPO FLORENTIA MDCCLXXXX."
Gift of John Vaughan, 1818.
(58.S.48)

ALEXANDER HAMILTON [2] (Fig. 17)

Cast after Giuseppe Ceracchi by J. Lanelli.
Plaster bust. Height 24″.
Cast in shoulder: "J. Lanelli N 435" and "Hamilton."
Gift of Mrs. Thomas Astley, 1840.
(58.S.7)

HERMAN HAUPT, 1817–1905

Civil and military engineer, inventor.
APS 1871.

General Haupt graduated from the United States Military Academy in 1835. His *General Theory of Bridge Construction* appeared in 1851 and long remained the authoritative treatise on this subject. His *Reminiscences*, published in 1901, gives the details of his contributions to railroad engineering and of the highly important role he played in the military operations of the Civil War.

By Anna Margaretta Archambault, 1917, from a photograph.
Oil on canvas. 50¼″ × 34″.
Signed on back: "General Herman Haupt / by A. M. Archambault—/ 1917."
Gift of the artist, 1946.
(58.P.73)

ISAAC MINIS HAYS, 1847–1925 (Fig. 49)

Physician, librarian, archivist.
APS 1886; Secretary 1897–1922; Librarian *pro-tem.* 1897–1898; Librarian 1898–1922.

Dr. Hays was first his father's assistant editor, then himself editor of the *American Journal of Medical Science.* He was for twenty years on the Library Committee of the College of Physicians of Philadelphia. As the Society's Librarian he completed the great task of repairing and mounting the Franklin Papers, "in such a way," he reported in 1900, "that it is believed that it will last as long as it is possible to preserve Mss." Through his efforts, the *Proceedings* was given more frequent publication. He acted as editor from 1898 to 1922, and as editor of the *Transactions* from 1898 to 1924. His *Chronology of Benjamin Franklin, 1706–90, Founder of the American Philosophical Society* was published in 1904, and in 1908 his five-volume *Calendar of the Papers of Benjamin Franklin.* The celebration in 1906 of the two hundredth anniversary of Franklin's birth was principally his work, although he remained in the background. The Society acknowledged his part by a standing vote of thanks at the General Meeting of April 20, 1906.

President Keen had written, "Dr. Hays' life was an ellipse with Benjamin Franklin and the American Philosophical Society in the 2 foci. . . . He knew the American Philosophical Society *au fond* better than any of the rest of us I am sure." Dr. Hays was Dean of the Wistar Association, and in 1917, to mark its centennial and the twenty-first year of Dr. Hays' secretaryship, the Association commissioned this portrait.

By Lazar Raditz, 1917.
Oil on canvas. 42½" × 36".
Signed (upper right): "Lazar Raditz / 1917."
Gift of the Wistar Association, 1917.
(58.P.23)

JOHN GOTTLIEB ERNESTUS HECKEWELDER, 1743– 1823 (Fig. 27)

Missionary, ethnologist.
APS 1797.

Heckewelder's association with the Indians began soon after his arrival in Pennsylvania from England, about 1754. From 1771 to 1786 he was their missionary from the Moravian Church. Because of the trust placed in him on both sides he was of service to the United States in negotiations with them. He spent the last years of his life writing his *Account of the History, Manners, and Customs of the Indian Natives, Who Once Inhabited Pennsylvania and the Neighboring States.* He had been in touch with Peter S. Du Ponceau on the progress of the work, and Du Ponceau, on reading the manuscript, predicted that it would have great success in both America and Europe. In a

45

letter to John Vaughan, April 30, 1818, he gave three reasons for his prediction:

1. It is written with the most unaffected simplicity, & yet with perfect clearness. You love the author & you are irresistably impelled to believe the Truth of what he says. In this respect it resembles Montaigne's Essays.

2. It differs from all other books written on the Indians [in] that it paints their fair side & makes the reader wish to live among them, as the reading of Robinson Crusoe has made many a boy wish to live on a desart island.

3. Without being so intended, it conveys the most Severe Satyre on Civilised Society, & all men love Satyre, see the Chapter on Ambition, p. 113. This will have a great affect in Europe. The more corrupt a nation is, the more it loves pictures of Virtue, which show them at a distance a different scene from their own.

The work was published first in the *Transactions* of the Historical and Literary Committee of 1819. Translations into German and French followed in 1821 and 1822. Du Ponceau's warm interest in it suggests that he may have commissioned the artist to paint Heckewelder's portrait. The painting came to the Society as Du Ponceau's gift. It has been variously attributed as the work of "Mr. Peale," and "Mr. R. Peale." The following is the concluding paragraph of a letter to Du Ponceau, dated from "Elizabeth town, May 3th 1822," and written by a German litterateur Gustav Anton von Seckendorff. Von Seckendorff, who called himself also "Patrick Peale," had recently arrived in this country, where he proposed to make his living as a painter. It appears from his letter that he had made a portrait of Du Ponceau:

Spring and country are in my favour and I, without high desires enjoy myself at those pleasures so quite however. Leiving on a farm of Mrs Niemoewitz and Major Kean I find myself in an element of piece very essential to me after a serious European life. Such as I lieve now my dooings *may* have the intensive success which I desire to give them. A few furnitures I buyed at New York and I lieve very simple, cheap and retired to my admiration of nature. Here I intend to remain till the spring 1823 or 1824. Here your likeness, dear Sir, will become somewhat more perfect then at Philadelphia. But, Sir, when at your house you offert me the payment for your likeness I refused it. Yet it would be of gread service to me now. Here it suppordes me and my mother in law for more than 6 weeks, and in Philadelphia it would have been spended in one fortnight. Will you kindly lieve me have the sayd 20 doll now. I shall send you, or bring to you, by a visit myself, your likeness in the course of one month.

A more extended picture I began already too and it has good suc-

46

cess. It is Abraham and Isaak. All my hopes must be founded now on some good pictures! When by them I shall have gained the first 4 or 500 Dollars and then I may soon be a citizen and settled in the United States of America.

Please to accept the respects of
Your
most humble and obedient Servant
De Seckendorff.

The little painting shows its subject just as Edward Rondthaler describes him in his *Life* of 1847, sitting "with his hands clasped upon his staff, his countenance beaming with peace and kindness."

Attributed to Gustav Anton von Seckendorff, *alias* Patrick Peale, *circa* 1822–1823.
Oil on canvas. 14 $\frac{5}{16}''$ × 12$\frac{1}{8}''$.
Gift of Peter Stephen Du Ponceau, 1824.
(58.P.32)

JOSEPH HENRY [1], 1797–1878

Physicist. First Secretary of the Smithsonian Institution.
APS 1835; Councillor 1841–1851.

Inevitably, Joseph Henry as a scientist has been compared to Franklin. It occurred in the *National Intelligencer's* announcement of his appointment to the new Smithsonian Institution, December 4, 1846:

Second, perhaps, to Franklin only, stands the name of the philosopher of Princeton. If Franklin discovered the identity between lightning and electricity, Henry has gone further, and reduced electric and magnetic action to the same laws.

It occurs also to the reader of Henry's own estimate of his career:

My life has been principally devoted to science and my investigations in different branches of physics have given me some reputation in the line of original discovery. I have sought, however, no patent for invention and solicited no remuneration for my labors, but have freely given the results to the world; expecting only in return to enjoy the consciousness of advancing science, the pleasure of discovering new truths, and the scientific reputation to which these labors would entitle me. (Thomas Coulson, *Joseph Henry: His Life and Work,* 339, Princeton, 1950.)

Shortly after Joseph Henry's death, the Minutes for December 6, 1878, carried:

A donation for the collection of portraits was received from Mr. Sol. W. Roberts . . . a portrait of the late Joseph Henry, in oils, framed

47

and endorsed as follows: "Prof. Joseph Henry, Secy of the Smithsonian Institution, &c. Born at Albany New York December 17th, 1797; Died at Washington, D.C. May 13th, 1878, in his eighty first year. This small portrait of Prof Henry is presented to the American Philosophical Society by Solomon W. Roberts, Civil Engineer, Philad. Dec. 1878."

By unidentified artist.
Oil on paper (?). $10\frac{1}{4}'' \times 8\frac{1}{4}''$.
Gift of Solomon W. Roberts, 1878.
(58.P.88)

JOSEPH HENRY [2] (Fig. 43)

Entries in his "Annual Record 1875" at the Smithsonian Institution record the painting of a portrait by Henry Ulke in that year:

Nov. 22 Sat to Mr. Ulke for my portrait to be exhibited at the centennial.

Nov. 27 Sat again to Ulke—a very tedious operation—was all the morning devoted to painting the pantaloons.

Dec. 2 (1?) Sat to Ulke for my portrait—worked on the face— a good likeness if viewed from a distance—bold in outline not finely worked up.

Members of the Society, eager to have on their walls a more monumental work than the small painting described above, circulated the following subscription paper for the purchase of a replica by Ulke of his earlier portrait:

The subscribers agree to contribute the sums set opposite to their names for the purpose of procuring the portrait of the late Professor Joseph Henry, to be presented to The American Philosophical Society.

The picture is a copy of the one exihibted by Mr. Henry Ulke, of Washington at the Centennial and The Academy of Fine Arts in 1876, and is to cost (without frame) $250.

He is painted by Mr. Ulke, and is now on exhibition, at Earle's Picture Gallery, Chestnut below 9th Street.
September, 1879.

By Henry Ulke, 1879, after his portrait of 1875.
Oil on canvas. $30'' \times 25''$.
Signed (lower right): Henry Ulke 1879."
Gift of friends: Alexander J. Cassat, George W. Childs, Samuel Dickson, Anthony J. Drexel, Frederick Fraley, Clement A. Griscom, Thomas C. Hand, E. Otis Kendall, John Lawrence LeConte, Frank L. Neall, Joseph Patterson, Charles Platt, George B. Roberts, Fairman Rogers, Thomas A. Scott, Frank Thomson, Charles Wheeler, Henry Winsor, Richard Wood, James A. Wright.
(58.P.8)

48

THOMAS HOPKINSON, 1709-1751

Jurist.

A founder and President of the American Philosophical Society of 1743.

Thomas Hopkinson's obituary appeared in the *Pennsylvania Gazette* of November 14, 1751:

Last week died here the honourable THOMAS HOPKINSON, Esq; Judge of the Admirality for this Province, one of the Governor's Council, and Prothonotary of the Court of Common Pleas for the County of Philadelphia, &c. . . .

In the same year appeared in London the *Experiments and Observations on Electricity, Made at Philadelphia in America, by Mr. Benjamin Franklin,* a work to which, as Franklin was careful to acknowledge, Hopkinson's friendly collaboration had contributed material of value. Hopkinson had been a founder of the Library Company, the College, the Philosophical Society —a friend, as Franklin wrote, "whose virtue and integrity, in every station of life, public and private, will ever make his Memory dear to those who knew him."

By Hermann F. Deigendesch, 1910, after a copy of a portrait attributed to Robert Feke.
Oil on canvas. 50" × 40½".
Gift of a number of subscribers, 1911.
(58.P.68)

FRIEDRICH HEINRICH ALEXANDER, BARON VON HUMBOLDT, 1769-1859 (Fig. 29)

Naturalist, explorer.

APS 1804.

Humboldt's election to the Society occurred during his visit to the United States after five years of study and travel in South America. At the Society's Humboldt Memorial Meeting in 1859, Alexander Dallas Bache said, "Humboldt's reputation was emphatically American. It was made on this continent. . . . It was here, in the heart of the Andes, and the peak of Chimborozo that he found the true field for his genius—in exploration, geology, botany." A portrait had been painted from life for the Society, but came into its possession only after the passage of many years. From Philadelphia, June 12, 1856, James Reid Lambdin has written to the Society:

Gentlemen,

I design to sail from this port for Europe, in the steamer of the 26th inst to be absent for a few months.

It is my desire whilst abroad to paint original portraits of several

49

of the most distinguished Savans of Europe, to be placed, eventually, I hope, in possession of the American Philosophical Society: whose aid I would respectfully invoke, inasmuch as it would be difficult to obtain the necessary sittings at the simple request of an humble individual like myself. I do not wish it understood however, that the Society are to be held pecuniary liable, or incur any responsibility whatever in the matter.

Should the Society think proper to give the subject their consideration at an early day, they will confer a favour on

Their obedient servt
J. R. Lambdin

Over thirty years later came:

1224 Chestnut Street
Phila. May 17th 87

Philip C. Garret Esq
Dear Sir
Having determined to close my Gallery of Portraits & Studio in the city I am desirous of placing the portraits, as far as possible, in situations where they will be appreciated. Among them is an original portrait of Humboldt half length size, 40.50, painted from studies from the life made in Berlin in 1856. The circumstances under which the portrait was painted were these. Having been appointed by the Smithsonian Institution of Washington its agent to carry out an important measure in Europe, it was suggested by Professor A D Bache and seconded by Henry D. Gilpin Esq. that I should paint for them a large portrait of Humboldt to be presented to the American Philosophical Society by the subscribing members. The letter of request to Humboldt was by Bache & readily assented to. Mr Gilpin writing to our American Minister Ex Govr Vroom, to further the objects as much as was in his power.

The portrait was not finished for some time after my return home, & was never seen by Prof Bache, who had fallen into bad health. Mr Gilpin saw it but once, & that was just previous to his fatal sickness. The portrait has been in the exhibitions New York Phila & Washington but with these exceptions, has never been out of my studio.

Nothing was ever said about the price by the gentlement before alluded to, but I was receiving at that period $500 for half lengths.

Respectfully yours,
J R Lambdin

My price for portraits of that size at the time when it was painted was $500. I will take for it, with its frame Three hundred & fifty dollars.

Philip C. Garrett wrote to Frederick Fraley, May 23, 1887:

The eminent portrait painter of our city, Mr. J. R. Lambdin, has in his studio, a large portrait of Humboldt, which was originally destined for the Philosophical Society, having been painted by him

50

from life for certain members of the Society with the intention of presenting it.

It appears to me to be an excellent likeness.

Mr. Lambdin is now 80 years of age, & is about giving up his studio.

It seems to me that the picture should be in the ownership of the Society, & if members agree with me in this opinion, I shall be glad to join with others in buying it.

I enclose Mr. Lambdin's letter, in a postscript to which he offers the picture & frame for $350.

Will it be a proper subject to submit to the society?

Philip C. Garrett, Daniel G. Brinton and Horace Jayne, as a committee, appealed for subscriptions in a broadside dated October 15, 1887, and the project was carried through successfully with the support of twenty-three contributing members.

By James Reid Lambdin, *circa* 1856–1857, from studies from life, 1856.

Oil on canvas. 50″ × 40″.

Gift of members: G. W. Anderson, John R. Baker, R. Meade Bache, George H. Boker, W. G. A. Bonwill, George W. Childs, E. W. Clark, J. M. DaCosta, Frederick Fraley, Philip C. Garrett, Horace Jayne, E. Otis Kendall, William V. McKean, J. Sargeant Price, James W. Robins, Moncure Robinson, J. R. Shipley, William P. Tatham, Frank Thomson, Richard Vaux, Joseph Wharton, Henry Winsor, and Richard Wood, 1887.

(58.P.59)

JOHN JAY, 1745–1829

Statesman, diplomat. Chief Justice of the Supreme Court of the United States.

APS 1780.

The Society's portrait, a small enamel "souvenir," was once owned by Alexander Chambers, of Newtown, Pennsylvania, an ardent admirer of Jay.

After an engraving by Pierre Eugène Du Simitière.
Battersea enamel. $1\frac{13}{16}″ \times 1\frac{3}{8}″$ (oval).
Inscribed: "J. JAY".
Gift of Miss Elizabeth Chambers, 1956.
(58.P.74)

HENRY LaBARRE JAYNE, 1857–1920

Lawyer, philanthropist.

APS 1898; Treasurer 1903–1920.

Roland S. Morris, in presenting the portrait of Henry LaBarre Jayne at the meeting of April 25, 1924, said:

51

He loved the riches of the mind and always thought of himself with characteristic modesty as a private enlisted for life in the adventurous search for truth. Above all he loved his fellow-man with an almost religious passion and no human soul was an alien to his broad and generous sympathies.

But it was his truly spiritual insight which gave to these affections and to the personality which unified them that sense of his continued presence which we feel today.

How natural—how inevitable—that when he left us in the body we, his friends, should seek to find some material expression of this continued presence in our lives. Thus spontaneously a group of his fellow-citizens, representatives of the varied interests of an active life, organized the JAYNE MEMORIAL FUND to hold, if I may so express it, something of his spirit for the generations to come, who knew him not in the flesh.

Out of this movement grew the Jayne Memorial Lectures—a permanent foundation adequately endowed, designed to give each year to some leader of thought an opportunity to present to the world the results of his research. . . . But we, his friends, his associates in various activities, longed for some memorial of him more personal than the foundation could be. So we turned to a great artist and asked him to express in bronze our memory of his ever youthful vigor and enthusiasm.

It is fitting, Mr. President, that the Trustees of the University Extension Society should place in the custody of the American Philosophical Society this memorial to our friend. To the University Extension Society Henry LaBarre Jayne gave unsparingly of his time and strength. To the American Philosophical Society with its fine traditions of truth and its achievements in the field of scientific research he gave affectionately the riches of his creative personality. We leave in your keeping this beautiful reminder of him amid the memorials of the great minds he loved and reverenced. In our hearts we retain the inspiration of his unselfish life, of his immortal spirit.

By Robert Tait McKenzie. 1924.

Bronze bas-relief. $34\frac{3}{4}'' \times 21\frac{1}{4}''$.

Signed and inscribed: "RTM [monogram] / 1914" and "HENRY LA BARRE JAYNE / 1857–1920 / A / GREAT CITIZEN / WHO GAVE GENEROUSLY / OF HIS TIME, HIS TALENTS / AND HIS FORTUNE TO THE / DIFFUSION OF KNOWLEDGE / THE PROGRESS OF THE FINE ARTS / THE DEVELOPMENT OF THE DRAMA / AND THE PROMOTION / OF CIVIL IDEALS."

Gift of the Trustees of the University Extension Society, 1924. (58.S.35)

THOMAS JEFFERSON [1], 1743–1826 (Fig. 14)

Statesman, scientist, amateur of the arts. Third President of the United States.

52

APS 1780; Councillor 1781–1786; 1818–1826; Vice-President 1791–1795; President 1797–1814.

Jefferson came to Paris as Franklin's successor at the Court of France. There his interest in the arts found full scope at once. Of the sculptor Houdon, who had made Franklin's bust, who was to make his own, and who was commissioned to make the full-length statue of Washington for the state of Virginia, he wrote in high praise as having "the reputation of being the first statuary in the world." It was not until 1789 that Houdon's bust of Jefferson was exhibited at the Salon as "M. Sesseron, envoyé des États de la Virginie." Although there were five casts of Houdon busts at Monticello, Jefferson seems to have kept none himself. It is believed, however, that he may have bought casts of his own portrait for friends. The Society's bust was at the Hall by 1811, and it may have been given by Jefferson to David Rittenhouse. On April 5, 1811, the Society

Resolved that a request be made to Mrs. Sergeant, for permission to remove the bust of Mr. Jefferson, in her possession, to our Hall and that Messrs. Vaughan & Patterson be a Committee to execute the same and when obtained, to have it bronzed.

On September 20, 1811,

Messrs. Patterson & Vaughan reported that they had executed the Commission given to them at the Meeting of 5 April to apply to Mrs. Elizabeth Sergeant for permission to remove to the Hall of the Society the Bust of their president Thomas Jefferson—Mrs. Sergeant granted the request, it has as directed been bronzed & is now placed in the Hall.

Mrs. Jonathan Dickinson Sergeant was a daughter of David Rittenhouse, and his executrix. While not precisely so stated, the bust appears to have come to the Society as her gift. In letters to Jefferson of 1814 and 1819 both Jonathan Williams and William Short informed their absent President of the presence of his portrait bust among the others at the Hall.

The bust has been restored to its original white color.

From the original by Jean Antoine Houdon, circa 1787.
Plaster bust. Height 29″.
Cut in back under shoulder: "T J."
Gift of Elizabeth Rittenhouse Sergeant, from the estate of her father, David Rittenhouse, 1811.
(58.S.22)

THOMAS JEFFERSON [2] (Fig. 15)

The Minutes for December 19, 1890, carried, "A plaster bust portrait of Jefferson, for the Society's Cabinet, was received

53

from Miss Emily Phillips, Philadelphia." The gift was a bas-relief profile by George M. Miller, an artist who had come to the United States from Scotland in the 1790's and who, by the time of his death in 1819, had achieved some reputation as a sculptor. Many of his portraits were in wax and in color, and the Society's appears to be a cast of one of these. The portrait was first described by Charles Henry Hart ("Life Portraits of Thomas Jefferson," *McClure's Magazine*, 11: 52, 1898), who states that it was

originally the property of Zeligman [*sic*] Phillips, one of the founders of the Pennsylvania Academy of the Fine Arts in 1805, a prominent criminal lawyer, and a pronounced follower of Jefferson's politics. From him it descended to his son, the late Hon. Henry M. Phillips, of Philadelphia. . . . It is inscribed with the date and artist's name, in the handwriting of its original owner, Zeligman Phillips.

This inscription, on a label of the back, reads: "Thomas Jefferson / 1803 / supposed to be by Muller or Miller."

By George M. Miller, 1803.
Plaster bas-relief. 6″ × 4¾″.
Gift of Miss Emily Phillips, 1890.
(58.S.42)

THOMAS JEFFERSON [3] (Fig. 13)

On January 26, 1821, the United States Military Academy, having already engaged Thomas Sully for the purpose, asked Jefferson to pose for a portrait to join the others of distinguished soldiers and citizens in the Academy's library. To this he acceded on February 13, regretting only that Mr. Sully might "consider the trouble of his journey and the employment of his fine pencil, as illy bestowed on an ottamy of 78." William Dunlap, whose *History of the Rise and Progress of the Arts of Design in the United States*, published in 1834, is derived largely from artists' autobiographical statements, records that Sully "visited the sage at Monticello, and in his house made a painting head size, of the venerable ex-president. The painter was an inmate of Monticello twelve days, and left the place with the greatest reluctance."

The life portrait painted at Monticello appears to be, actually, that now owned by the Society. The Minutes for June 18, 1830, carried:

Mr. Short presented to the Society a Portrait of Thomas Jefferson, many years President of the United States, painted by Thomas Sully, from which he painted the full length picture for the Military Academy at West Point.

54

By Thomas Sully, 1821.
Oil on canvas. 30" × 25".
The original canvas had reportedly had on the back the TS monogram and "From Jefferson 1821." The modern re-backing is not marked.
Gift of William Short, 1830.
(58.P.12)

JOHN PAUL JONES, 1747–1792

Naval officer.

By Wedgwood, nineteenth century, after model of *circa* 1790. Modeled by Augustin Dupré, after the medal by I. Dassier et Fils (Records, Buten Museum of Wedgwood).
Ceramic medallion. White on black jasper dip. Diam. 2 $\frac{3}{16}$".
Impressed on back: "P. Jones" and "WEDGWOOD."
Provenance unknown.
(58.S.61)

ELISHA KENT KANE [1], 1820–1857

Physician, naval officer, Arctic explorer.
APS 1851.

The tragedy of Dr. Kane's early death, his health undermined by his Arctic expeditions in search of Sir John Franklin, was felt throughout the world. It was the passing of a hero, mourned by friends, colleagues, and by all his countrymen. He had died at Havana, February 16, 1857. The Society, at a special meeting, February 27,

Resolved, that a portrait of Dr. Kane be placed in the Hall of the Society, as a continuing memorial of him, which may silently teach us, and those who are to come after us, how to pursue and adorn science with persevering energy, truth, modesty and excellence.

At the meeting of March 20,

On motion of Dr. William Harris, it was agreed that a committee be appointed to consult with Mr. J. R. Lambdin, relative to the painting of a portrait of the late Dr. E. K. Kane, and to report to the Society at a future meeting. Dr. W. Harris, Mr. Justice, and Prof. Trego, were appointed to the committee.

At the meeting of April 3, it was

Reported that Mr. Lambdin offered to paint a portrait of a size corresponding to those already in the Hall of the Society, for one hundred dollars:—Whereupon, the committee was authorized to contract with Mr. Lambdin for the execution of the portrait, and an appropriation of $100 was made to defray the cost of the same.

On May 1, the portrait was said to be "now nearly completed."

55

By James Reid Lambdin, 1857, probably after an ambrotype by Brady.
Oil on canvas. 30″ × 25⅛″.
Painted on order, 1857.
(58.P.9)

ELISHA KENT KANE [2] (Fig. 46)

By Peter Reniers, 1857.
Plaster bust. Height 28″.
Signed (in shoulder): "Peter Reniers, Sculptor Philada. 1857."
Provenance unknown.
(58.S.3)

JOHN KINTZING KANE, 1795–1858 (Fig. 37)

Jurist.

APS 1825: Secretary 1828–1849; Vice-President 1849–1857; President 1857–1858.

At a special meeting, February 23, 1858, almost exactly a year after that called upon the news of the death of Elisha Kent Kane, the Society met again to hear the formal announcement of the passing of his father, John Kintzing Kane, Judge of the United States District Court for the Eastern District of Pennsylvania, public-spirited citizen of Philadelphia, and its President since the preceding year. At the meeting of a week later, April 2,

On motion of Dr. Wm. Harris, a committee, consisting of Dr. Harris, Mr. Dunlap and Mr. Patterson, was appointed to procure a portrait of Judge Kane, late President of the Society.

On March 16, 1860,

Dr. Harris, from the committee appointed to procure a portrait of Judge Kane, reported it finished and in the Hall of the Society, and presented a bill for painting, framing, &c., which was ordered to be paid.

By Thomas Hicks, 1859, after a photograph or earlier portrait.
Oil on canvas. 33⅛″ × 28⅞″.
Signed (lower left): "T. Hicks / 1859."
Painted on order, 1858–1859.
(58.P.54)

WILLIAM WILLIAMS KEEN, 1837–1932 (Fig. 48)

Physician, surgeon, teacher, editor.

APS 1884; Councillor 1905–1908; President 1908–1918.

His portrait shows Dr. Keen wearing the cap and gown of a

56

Doctor of Laws of the University of Saint Andrews, from which Franklin had received the same degree. He is seated in the Presidential Chair, formerly Franklin's, and beyond him is seen a bust of Franklin after Houdon. The Minutes of April 19, 1913, record:

A portrait of William W. Keen, M.D., LL.D., President of the Society, was presented by Joseph G. Rosengarten, A.M., LL.D., on behalf of the subscribers.

Mr. Rosengarten said, in part:

On behalf of the subscribers, I have the honor and privilege of presenting to the Society, the portrait of our President, Dr. William W. Keen, by Robert Vonnoh.

Among the one hundred and twenty-nine subscribers,—a list will be handed to the Secretaries for preservation among its records, will be found the names of many representatives of institutions of learning, many men noted in science and letters, who thus testify their grateful sense of Dr. Keen's great services to the Philosophical Society, both as member and as President.

By Robert William Vonnoh, 1912.
Oil on canvas. $42\frac{1}{8}'' \times 38''$.
Signed (lower left): "Robt. Vonnoh 1912—c—"
Gift of friends, 1913.
(58.P.58)

MARIE JOSEPH PAUL YVES ROCH GILBERT DU MOTIER, MARQUIS DE LAFAYETTE [1], 1757–1834

Soldier, statesman.
APS 1781.

The Wedgwood medallions of Lafayette were first published with the portraits of other French notables for sale in France in that period before reform had been succeeded by violent revolution and war with England. Lafayette, therefore, is represented not as an American officer, but in his uniform as colonel-general of the National Guard of Paris and in the period, 1789–1791, of his greatest influence upon the history of his own country. One of the two medals which he wears at his lapel, however, is the "Eagle" of the Society of the Cincinnati.

By Wedgwood, nineteenth century, from model of *circa* 1789–1791.
Ceramic medallion. White on gray jasper. Diam. $2\frac{3}{16}''$.
Impressed on back: "Lafayette" and "WEDGWOOD."
Provenance unknown.
(58.S.78)

57

MARQUIS DE LAFAYETTE [2]

By Wedgwood, nineteenth century, from model of *circa* 1789–1791.
Ceramic medallion. White on gray jasper. $4\,\frac{7}{16}\,'' \times 3\frac{3}{8}''$ (oval).
Impressed on back: "Lafayette" and "WEDGWOOD."
Provenance unknown.
(58.S.59)

MARQUIS DE LAFAYETTE [3]

By Wedgwood. A late version of the above.
Ceramic medallion. White on blue jasper dip with white self frame.
$4\,\frac{7}{16}'' \times 3\,\frac{7}{16}''$ (oval).
Inscribed on back: "LAFAYETTE / 1757–1834." Impressed on
back: WEDGWOOD."
Provenance unknown.
(58.S.60)

MARQUIS DE LAFAYETTE [4] (Fig. 18)

The Society's plaster bust of Lafayette is believed to be an
example of the work of a Neapolitan sculptor and painter who
spent a number of years in the United States, contributed to the
adornment of the capitol at Washington, and was in Philadelphia, 1824–1825, during Lafayette's sensational American
tour. It is a rare example of the overflowing homage paid everywhere to the "National Guest," a warm, emotional outpouring
of patriotic affection, to which his fellow members at Philosophical Hall contributed from full hearts their share.

Attributed to E. Luigi Persico, 1824.
Plaster bust. Height $24\frac{1}{2}''$.
Gift of Dr. Nathaniel Chapman, 1829.
(58.S.5)

SAMUEL PIERPONT LANGLEY, 1834–1906

Astronomer, physicist, inventor. Third Secretary of the Smithsonian Institution.
APS 1875; Vice-President 1902–1905.

Langley's great contributions to meteorology and aeronautics
carried on primary interests of the Society's founder, and his
selfless dedication to research was equal to Franklin's. Of him,
in accepting his portrait at the meeting of April 24, 1914, Vice-
President Pickering said:

My acquaintance with Samuel Pierpont Langley goes back to the
winter of 1870, when we crossed the ocean together to observe the
total eclipse of the sun, in Spain. We maintained an unbroken
friendship until his death, nearly forty years later. As a young man

he was enthusiastic, and full of hope for the future. . . . In accepting the position of secretary of the Smithsonian Institution, he stipulated that he should be enabled to continue his scientific investigations. . . . For many years the question of artificial flight had an absorbing interest for him. His investigations were long and laborious, and finally he attained success with a small model. When constructing a larger instrument, his sensitiveness induced him to avoid publicity, thus greatly annoying those whose business it is to keep the public informed of the latest news. They had their revenge when a misplaced nail in his launching apparatus ruined his aeroplane on its trial, and the subsequent ridicule and criticism saddened his last days, and shortened his life. The success of aerial navigation is largely due to his work, which has only received the credit it deserves since his death. . . .

Langley, by his devotion to the advancement of human knowledge, well deserves a place among those whose portraits adorn these walls, and in the name of the American Philosophical Society held at Philadelphia for Promoting Useful Knowledge, I accept this portrait and extend grateful acknowledgments to the donors.

By Lazar Raditz, from a photograph of *circa* 1894.
Oil on canvas. 30″ × 25″.
Signed (lower right): "Lazar Raditz."
Gift of members: Cyrus Adler, Carl Hazard Barus, Louis A. Bauer, Alexander Graham Bell, John A. Brashaer, George F. Edmunds, George Gray, George E. Hale, David Jayne Hill, Thomas Corwin Mendenhall, Charles E. Munroe, Edward Leamington Nichols, Richard Olney, Henry F. Osborn, Edward C. Pickering, Raphael Pumpelly, Edward Bennett Rosa, Frank Schlesinger, Samuel W. Stratton, Mayer Sulzberger, Elihu Thomson, Otto Hilgard Tittman, Charles D. Walcott, Andrew D. White, and Robert S. Woodward, 1914.
(58.P.13)

ANTOINE LAURENT LAVOISIER, 1734–1794

Chemist.
APS 1775.
The small circular bas-relief of Lavoisier who, with his wife, was so close to Franklin as friend and collaborator, is of singular rarity and interest. No other example is known. It has not been determined whether the portrait is from life or, as is somewhat more probable, was made after the great chemist's tragic death at the guillotine. If the latter be true, the likeness would appear to have been taken from the Houdon bust, and the work may be assumed to have had some connection with "La Pompe Funèbre de Lavoisier au Lycée des Arts" of October 22, 1795. At that time, when political changes had made it possible to

do so, his friends and colleagues united in this and other events honoring his memory. It is known that engraved portraits were given to subscribers to a monument in his honor, and this medallion may have been intended for a similar purpose.

By an unidentified artist, *circa* 1795.
Plaster bas-relief. Diameter 7".
Inscribed: "Lavoisier, membre du lycée des arts."
Gift of Dr. John Redman Coxe, 1804.
(58.S.43)

HENRY CHARLES LEA, 1825–1909

Publisher, historian.
APS 1867.
Portraits of Isaac Lea and his son, Henry Charles Lea, were presented to the Society on January 20, 1911, at a meeting in which four other organizations participated, the Historical Society of Pennsylvania, the Library Company of Philadelphia, the University of Pennsylvania, and the Academy of Natural Sciences of Philadelphia. Dr. S. Weir Mitchell in presenting the portrait of Henry Charles Lea said:

I have had the honor of being selected by the family and friends of Mr. Henry Charles Lea to present to the Philosophical Society the portrait of our greatest historian. The portrait I thus place in the custody of the Society is a copy of the well-known portrait by Vonnoh, painted eighteen years ago, and is regarded by those who knew Mr. Lea best as an excellent picture of the man as he was. But that responsive face could never be so put on canvas as to recall for me the change from the grave scholarly look of attention to the smile which welcomed a friend to the privilege of the social hour; alas! here the artist fails us—
"For painting mute and motionless
Steals but a glance of time."

By Hugh Henry Breckenridge, 1910, after Robert William Vonnoh, 1896.
Oil on canvas. 50⅛" × 40".
Inscribed on back: "Copy by Hugh H. Breckenridge, 1910, of Portrait of / Henry Charles Lea of Philadelphia / Original by Robert Vonnoh, 1896."
Gift of the Family of Henry Charles Lea, 1911.
(58.P.55)

ISAAC LEA, 1792–1886 (Fig. 39)

Malacologist, publisher.
APS 1828; Curator 1831–1839; Councillor 1843–1858; Vice-President 1858–1877.

60

Isaac Lea, with his enormous bibliography on shells, contributed also many new discoveries to geology and paleontology. His collection of mollusks and snails is at the United States National Museum as is also his collection of gems (he had been the first in America to enter microscopic mineralogy). He was seventy-five years of age when his son, Henry Charles Lea, was elected to the Society and they were members together for almost twenty years. With Mathew Carey (father-in-law of one and grandfather of the other) they represented a continuity of some hundred and thirty years, friendships with Washington and Lafayette at one end, at the other friendships with Woodrow Wilson and others of his era. His portrait was presented to the Society in 1911, simultaneously with that of his son (see above). It was described upon the occasion by President Keen as "The portrait of Mr. Isaac Lea, a striking copy of Mr. Uhle's by Mr. Thomas P. Anschutz, of the Academy of the Fine Arts."

By Thomas Pollock Anshutz, *circa* 1911, after Bernard Uhle, 1879. Oil on canvas. 50″ × 42¾″.
Gift of the family of Henry Charles Lea, 1911.
(58.P.53)

JOHN LAWRENCE LeCONTE, 1825–1883

Physician, entomologist.
APS 1853; Secretary 1855–1880; Vice-President 1880–1883.

LeConte was the first to map the faunal areas of the United States. A United States Medical Inspector *circa* 1860–1865, Chief Clerk at the United States Mint at Philadelphia, 1878–1883, President of the American Association for the Advancement of Science, 1874, his interests extended far beyond these spheres, and his contributions range beyond his chosen field of entomology into geology, vertebrate paleontology, zoology, and even the social sciences. J. Peter Lesley spoke eloquently of the comprehension of his imaginative and "well equipped mind" at the meeting of November 16, 1883:

It is a vulgar prejudice to suppose that a life spent counting the number of segments and legs of bugs, and describing the microscopic foliation of their antennae, incapacitates a man from comprehending the Mechanique Celeste or the writings of Plotinus; for the enjoyment of the Mahabahrata, or the safe conduct of his hereditary estate. What stamps the character of LeConte as a genius is precisely what gives the lie to this vulgar prejudice. He was as fine a mathematician as he was minutely true with the microscope. His wide and varied learning checked any tendency to narrowness in study, and gave him a power and richness of language which reacted on his reason to enrich it with a copious store of generous and noble ideas.

61

Henry Ulke, artist and entomologist, had written to Dr. LeConte from New York, February 12, 1857, with an invitation which suggests that his portrait may have been painted soon after:

Dear Doctor:

When I had the pleasure of seeing you at your house last fall you were kind enough to show me a little circular giving the description of coleopterous insects and the way to obtain them. I want to interest some Americans who are not familiar with the matter. If you have one or two left—I would feel greatly obliged. Will you be kind enough to let me know at your earliest convenience. I am very anxious to see you in New York—if only for a few days—it would give me the opportunity to make a good picture of you, which I know would give great satisfaction to your family and also to yourself.

Hoping to hear from you very soon, I remain your

Sincere
Henry Ulke.

It was not, however, until March 15, 1895, that the Minutes carried:

A portrait of the late Dr. John L. LeConte was presented on behalf of the donor, Mrs. LeConte, by Dr. Horn who referred to the services to science rendered by Dr. LeConte. Dr. J. C. Morris followed with a tribute to the memory of Dr. LeConte's personal and professional career and moved a vote of thanks to Mrs. LeConte for the gift of the portrait.

By Henry Ulke.
Oil on canvas. 27" × 22".
Signed (lower right): "H. Ulke."
Gift of Mrs. John Lawrence LeConte, 1895.
(58.P.4)

JOSEPH LEIDY [1], 1823–1891

Naturalist, anatomist, paleontologist.
APS 1849.

Paleontology offered to Leidy, as Henry Fairfield Osborn said, the "virgin field of our then virgin West." Within his work were mineralogy, comparative anatomy, zoology, and botany. His facts anticipated Darwin and Pasteur. On March 4, 1860, Charles Darwin wrote to him:

Your note has pleased me more than you could readily believe; for I have during a long time heard all good judges speak of your paleontological labours in terms of the highest respect. Most paleontologists (with some few good exceptions) entirely despise my work: consequently approbation from you has gratified me much. . . . Your

62

sentence that you have some interesting facts "in support of the doctrine of selection which I shall report at a favorable opportunity" has delighted me even more than the rest of your note.

Leidy said of himself that he was "too busy to theorize or make money."

Death mask, 1891.
Plaster. Height 11½″.
Provenance unknown.
(58.S.33)

JOSEPH LEIDY [2]

At the meeting of February 2, 1900, a letter from Dr. Samuel G. Dixon was read, presenting on behalf of a few friends a portrait of Dr. Leidy

by Mr. James L. Wood, copied from that by Mr. Bernard Uhle, in the Academy of Natural Sciences of Philadelphia. On Motion the best thanks of the Society were ordered to be transmitted to Dr. Dixon and the other friends.

By James L. Wood, circa 1900, after a portrait by Bernard Uhle, 1889, perhaps from a photograph.
Oil on canvas. 30″ × 25 ⅙″.
Gift of friends, 1900.
(58.P.7)

J. PETER LESLEY, 1819–1903

Geologist, librarian.

APS 1856; Librarian 1858–1885; Secretary 1859–1887; Vice-President 1887–1898.

Peter Lesley, Jr., disliking his baptismal name, placed the J. (for Junior) before it, and usually signed himself "J. P. Lesley." J. Peter Lesley is the form now accepted in the Society's records and elsewhere. Lesley's *Manual of Coal and its Topography*, 1856, and his *Iron Manufacturers' Guide*, 1859, were landmarks in the development of geological science. His enunciation of the principles governing the relation of structural geology to topography were important to the rising oil industry. As head of the Second Geological Survey of Pennsylvania (1873–1887) he produced more than a hundred publications. For approximately thirty years he acted as both Librarian and Secretary of the Society, cataloguing the Library with its first use of cards for the purpose, and taking at the same time entire charge of the Society's publications. His paper on the "Classification of Books," published in the *Annual Report* of the Smithsonian

63

Institution, 1862, is a fundamental and charming contribution to the principles of a young science. Library classification he declared to be "A reasonable arrangement in the hands of man ... a call to the soul, to be obeyed."

The general library, therefore, is a picture of a generous intellect, well stored, well ordered, and open to enlargement in all directions.

Its compartments represent the grand natural divisions of knowledge.

Its classifications should be in an ascending and advancing series.

Its treasures, like those of memory, should be preserved in the natural order of time, and the natural order of space should be ancillary and complementary, wherever applicable.

These are the maxims by which the cataloguing of the library of the American Philosophical Society has been governed.

Mrs. Lesley, his assistant in cataloguing, was the original of "The Lady from Philadelphia" in Lucretia Peabody Hale's popular *Peterkin Papers*. Their daughter, Margaret Lesley (Mrs. Henry K. Bush-Brown), was an artist and the painter of this portrait. Hers also was the portrait of Frederick Fraley (*q.v.*). Both paintings were presented to the Society by the same group of donors, May 20, 1898. Upon that occasion William A. Ingham referred to the Lesley portrait as

to me a most speaking likeness. It shows him as I have seen him a hundred times sitting in his chair, roused up from a reverie by some remark, whether opposing his views or corroborating them (it made little difference), but rousing him up and starting him off, active and alert on an animated discourse which might last an hour.

By Margaret Lesley Bush-Brown, *circa* 1894–1895.
Oil on canvas. 39¼″ × 29½″.
Gift of members and friends (see Fraley, Frederick, for list of donors), 1898.
(58.P.30)

GEORGE WALTER MELVILLE, 1841–1912

Naval officer, explorer, inventor, engineer.
APS 1897.

After notable service in the Civil War and in polar exploration, 1873–1884, Melville became Chief of the Bureau of Steam Engineering. Here, among other valuable contributions, he established postgraduate schools in naval engineering, published important works on the Nicaraguan canal route, the strategic value of Hawaii, the submarine as a weapon of naval warfare. The Society owns a cast of the artist's model of the bronze statue erected to him at League Island Park (Roosevelt Park), South

64

Philadelphia, in 1923, the likeness in which appears to have been taken from the bust made from life in 1895 by Henry Jackson Ellicott.

By Samuel Murray, 1904, probably after the bust by Henry Jackson Ellicott, 1895.
Plaster standing figure. Height 25½".
Inscribed: "Samuel Murray / Copyright / 1904."
Provenance unknown.
(58.S.34)

FRANÇOIS ANDRÉ MICHAUX, 1770–1855

Botanist.
APS 1809.

One of the portraits of French savants painted by Rembrandt Peale on his two visits to Paris, 1808–1810, was that of François André Michaux, who was then compiling his *Histoire des Arbres Forestiers de l'Amérique Septentrionale*. This work, published 1810–1813, continued in larger range that begun by his father with a study of the American oaks. The picture, commissioned by Charles Willson Peale for the gallery of his Philadelphia Museum, is listed in the Museum catalogue of 1813 as

No. 112. MICHAUX, Botanist, whose elegant and useful work on the forest trees of America, now publishing at Paris, will establish his reputation.

At the sale of the museum portraits, October 6, 1854, this one was purchased by Dr. Joseph Carson, at whose desire it was presented after his death to the Society. The Minutes of March 19, 1880, record:

Donation for the Cabinet.—Mr. Hampton L. Carson presented, on the part of his sisters and himself, in fulfillment of his father's wishes, to the cabinet of the Society, a portrait in oils of M. François André Michaux, the botanist, who died at Paris, October 23, 1855, aetat 85.

Mr. Fraley returned the thanks of the Society for so interesting and valuable a relic of our distinguished fellow-member, who exhibited in his lifetime so great an attachment for the Society, and in his will such confidence in the honor of its traditions as to make it the trustee of a fund which he bequested for Silviculture in America.

Mr. E. K. Price also described the amicable relations which existed between M. Michaux and the Society, claiming the privilege of doing so on the ground that the Society had conferred on him the duty of carrying out the designs of M. Michaux according to the plan adopted by the Committee and approved by the Society, and sketched the principal features of that plan—the planting of the

65

Michaux grove—and the organization of Prof. Rothrock's annual course of public lectures in the Park.

By Rembrandt Peale, *circa* 1808–1810.
Oil on canvas. 28¼" × 23¼".
Gift of Dr. Joseph Carson, received 1880.
(58.P.38)

ALBERT ABRAHAM MICHELSON, 1852–1931

Physicist.
APS 1902; Vice-President 1909–1919.

Michelson's bas-relief portrait was made soon after he became head of the Department of Physics at the University of Chicago in 1892. The publication of his *Velocity of Light* followed in 1902, and of his *Light Waves and their Uses* in 1903. The Nobel Prize for Physics, 1907, was among his many awards. His invention of the interferometer and his accomplishments with this delicate instrument were at the core of his life work. He said:

One comes to regard the machine as having a personality—I had almost said a feminine personality—requiring humoring, coaxing, cajoling, even threatening. But finally one realizes that the personality is that of an alert and skillful player in an intricate but fascinating game, who will take immediate advantage of the mistakes of his opponent, who "springs" the most disconcerting surprises, who never leaves any result to chance, but who nevertheless plays fair, in strict accordance with the rules he knows, and makes no allowance if you do not. When you learn them, and play accordingly, the game progresses as it should. (*Biographical Memoirs, National Academy of Science* 29: 138, 1938.)

By Katherine M. Cohen, 1893.
Plaster bas-relief. 20¼" × 14½".
Signed (lower left): "K. M. Cohen / sc— / 1893."
Gift of the artist, 1911.
(58.S.38)

The Genius of Franklin (Fig. 58). BY GIULIO MONTEVERDE

Among all the works of art composed in homage to Benjamin Franklin, Monteverde's *Genius* is unique. Spirited and free, it honors its subject with both a lighter and a surer touch than any other has achieved. It was first brought to the attention of the Society by Antonio Pace, and is best described in Dr. Pace's *Benjamin Franklin and Italy*:

By all odds the most original piece of art inspired by Franklin in the nineteenth century was the statue by the Milanese sculptor

66

Giulio Monteverde, a provocative artist whose work is both a reflection of the Risorgimento and an adumbration of the New Italy. In his art he rebelled against the academic, neo-Hellenistic canons in which he had himself been schooled. His three most important works—"The Young Columbus," "The Genius of Franklin," and "Edward Jenner"—attest to his intense concern with the theme of science and its implications for human progress. The "Genius of Franklin" catapulted him into European fame. The statue is not a likeness, but a symbolic interpretation of the youthful vigor and irreverence of Franklin's thought in subjugating the forces of nature. A pertly smiling winged sprite, gracefully entwined about a conductor on a housetop, seems to be making sport of guiding a bit of lightning into the chain that leads down from the rod. The unorthodox mixture of crude realism and bold symbol shocked the purists, who rallied about Pietro Tenerani, the leader of the classicists, to condemn Monteverde's creation. The bitter debate reached the heights of its acrimony when an implacable enemy compared Monteverde's sprite wrapped around the lightning rod to a spitted pigeon. The "Genius of Franklin" was none the less the sensation of the exhibition of 1872 in Milan, won the only government prize assigned for sculpture, and was purchased by The Khedive of Egypt, who further honored its creator with the cross of the Egyptian Order.

... As if out of gratitude to the man to whom he owed his first real fame, Monteverde placed a replica of "The Genius of Franklin" in a niche in the cornice of his home and studio in Rome, where it still stands today. What more appropriate than the saucy sprite should smile perpetually down upon the Piazza dell'Independenza? (*Mem. Amer. Philos. Soc.* 47: 296–297, 1958.)

By Giulio Monteverde, 1872.
Bronze figure. Height 26¾".
Signed on base: "Monteverde."
Purchased 1949.
(58.S.79)

ROLAND SLETOR MORRIS, 1874–1945 (Fig. 53)

Lawyer, administrator, diplomat.
APS 1922; President 1932–1942; Councillor 1942–1945.

Trained as a lawyer, Roland S. Morris practiced that profession in Philadelphia and was Professor of International Law in the University of Pennsylvania. President Wilson appointed him Ambassador to Japan, 1917–1921. At the end of World War I, he undertook a special diplomatic mission to Siberia. As President of the Society at a time when its financial resources were growing rapidly, he took an active part in the revision of its organization, policies, and management.

By Cameron Burnside, 1941.
Oil on canvas. 34" × 28".
Signed (lower right): "CAMERON BURNSIDE 1941."
Painted on order, 1941.
(58.P.18)

JOHN NAPIER, 1550–1617

Mathematician, inventor of logarithms.
For the donor's account of this small portrait of "Napier of Merchiston," see Buchan above. An engraving after the drawing appears as frontispiece in the Earl of Buchan's biography of Napier, and is illustrated in *Proc. Amer. Philos. Soc.* 94: 285, 1950.

By John Brown, after a portrait of *circa* 1616 in family ownership.
Pencil on ivory. 2⅜" × 1⅞" (oval).
Gift of the Earl of Buchan, 1795.
(58.P.82)

SIMON NEWCOMB, 1835–1909

Astronomer.
APS 1878; Vice-President 1905–1909.
Newcomb, the first American since Franklin to become a member of the Institut de France, used to say that, while astronomy was his vocation, political economy was his avocation. In later life he cooperated with A. A. Michelson in determining the velocity of light. Vice-President Pickering, in accepting the gift of his portrait for the Society at the meeting of April 23, 1910, commented upon the breadth of his interests:

A striking characteristic of the work of Newcomb was its versatility. Both astronomers and mathematicians regarded him as a leader, while his contributions to philosophy, to political economy and to other sciences were numerous and valuable. It was curious to see how, after devoting a life to the older astronomy, he became deeply interested in astrophysics, at an age when many men cease to do useful work.

The excellent portrait before you is especially welcome since it is the gift of many, not a few, of his admirers. As it hangs on the wall of this room it should serve as a model to us all. What happier lot can be asked for a man who, after retirement for age from the service of the United States, could continue his work with the greatest vigor, could live to see the greater part of it completed and who retained his intellectual powers to the end?

68

By Harold L. MacDonald, 1909, after his portrait of *circa* 1899, based
on a photograph of 1897.
Oil on canvas. 30″ × 25″.
Gift of members, 1910.
(58.P.10)

SIR ISAAC NEWTON [1], 1642–1727

Natural philosopher. President of the Royal Society, London,
1703–1727.
The Royal Society's congratulatory letter to the American
Philosophical Society, February 4, 1943, was accompanied by
the gift of a portrait of Newton:

On behalf of the President, Council and Fellows of the Royal
Society of London, I write to send the American Philosophical
Society hearty greetings on the occasion of the 200th anniversary of
its foundation by Benjamin Franklin. We are proud to recall that
not only was the founder a Fellow of our Society, but also that he
used its organization as a model for your Society.

We cannot allow the occasion to pass without offering the American Philosophical Society some token of our esteem, and it seems
fitting, now that we have so recently celebrated the tercentenary of
the birth of Isaac Newton, to offer you a small miniature of Newton,
painted in the latter part of the eighteenth century.

By an unidentified eighteenth-century artist, derived from the portrait
by John Vanderbank, 1725.
Miniature on ivory. 1¼″ × 1⅛″ (oval).
Gift of the Royal Society, London, 1943.
(58.P.61)

SIR ISAAC NEWTON [2]

By an unidentified artist, derived from the portrait by John Vanderbank, 1725.
Oil on canvas. 30″ × 25″.
Purchased 1947.
(58.P.6)

SIR ISAAC NEWTON [3]

The Society's small bust of Newton represents a late and popular version of the life-size portrait bust by Roubiliac which appears, in bronze, in the background of Benjamin Franklin's
portrait by David Martin.

Cast of a Wedgwood pottery bust, derived from the bust of Louis
François Roubiliac, 1751.
Plaster bust. Height 17″.
Provenance unknown.
(58.S.16)

SIR ISAAC NEWTON [4]

By Wedgwood, *circa* 1905. Model by A. H. Bentley, from model at-
tributed to Hoskins and Grant, 1787, after the bust by Roubi-
liac.
Ceramic plaque. White on black jasper dip. $12\frac{1}{8}″ \times 8\frac{9}{16}″$.
Inscribed in relief on the field: "NEWTON." Impressed on back:
"WEDGWOOD / o."
Provenance unknown.
(58.S.47)

GEORGE ORD, 1781–1866

Naturalist, philologist.
APS 1817; Secretary 1820–1828, 1829–1832; Vice-President
1832–1836; Councillor 1836–1842; Librarian and Treasurer
1842–1848.

George Ord was a Philadelphia businessman whose rigorous
standards of excellence set him, at times unhappily, apart from
many of his colleagues and somewhat lessened the great influence his contributions to zoology, ornithology, and philol-
ogy might otherwise have given him. As Librarian and Treasurer of the Society, he broke with the old, informal practices
and inaugurated an advance toward modern administration.

By J. Henry Smith, 1894, after John Neagle's portrait of 1829.
Oil on canvas. $29\frac{5}{8}″ \times 25\frac{1}{8}″$.
Signed (lower left): "J. Henry Smith / after / John Neagle."
Gift of members: Henry C. Baird, Daniel G. Brinton, S. S. Castner,
Jr., Clarence H. Clark, Frederick Fraley, George H. Horn,
William J. Potts, Joseph G. Rosengarten, W. S. W. Ruschen-
berger, Lewis A. Scott, William P. Tatham, 1894.
(58.P.64)

ROBERT PATTERSON, 1743–1824 (Fig. 19)

Mathematician. Director of the United States Mint.
APS 1783; Librarian 1788; Secretary 1784–1797; Curator
1797–1799; Vice-President 1799–1819; President 1819–1824.

A native of northern Ireland who had come, penniless, to
America at the age of twenty-five, Dr. Patterson established himself as a teacher of navigation and mathematics, served as Bri-
gade Major during the Revolution, became Professor of Mathe-

70

matics and the Vice Provost of the University of Pennsylvania. Thomas Jefferson appointed him Director of the United States Mint in 1805 In his "Obituary Notice," Chief Justice William Tilghman wrote of him:

Nature had been liberal to Dr. Patterson. She endowed him with strength of body and solidity of understanding. His mind was peculiarly adapted to the exact sciences, in which he made considerable progress, and was certainly a distinguished teacher. He was not however satisfied in any case with mere abstract mathematical truth, but always sought for its application to some practical purpose. This appears from his works, which are all elementary, and his numerous papers published in the Transactions of our Society.

By Rembrandt Peale, 1830, a replica of his portrait of *circa* 1812. Oil on canvas. $30\frac{1}{8}'' \times 25\frac{1}{16}''$. Gift of a number of members, 1830. (58.P.48)

ROBERT MASKELL PATTERSON [1], 1787-1854

Physician, chemist.

APS 1809; Secretary 1813-1825; Vice-President 1825-1830, 1836-1845; President 1849-1853.

After taking his medical degree and completing his education in chemistry with Sir Humphrey Davy in England, Dr. Patterson became Professor of Natural Philosophy, Chemistry and Mathematics at the University of Pennsylvania. In 1828 he accepted a professorship at the University of Virginia, and in 1835 returned to Philadelphia as Director of the United States Mint, a post which his father, Robert Patterson (*q.v.*), had held before him.

A few months after his death, a portrait of him came to the Society as the gift of his widow. It was transmitted, April 20, 1855, by a letter from his son, Robert Patterson, who wrote in fuller explanation some years later, January 30, 1889, in a letter addressed to Secretary Henry Phillips:

The Portrait of my father is a replica by Mr. Samuel F. DuBois of an original by him in possession of our family. I think it was not taken from life, but from a photograph, aided by the memory of the artist, who was my father's nephew, and brought by various circumstances into intimate association with him. It is a *likeness*, but fails to express the refinement & intelligence characteristic of the original. The portrait was presented by my Mother.

In a later letter, May 16, 1896, he added that the artist was an "Uncle of our Secretary DuBois," and the painting, he believed, a replica of that at the United States Mint.

71

By Samuel F. DuBois, 1855, replica of his earlier portrait.
Oil on canvas. $30\frac{1}{8}'' \times 25\frac{1}{8}''$.
Inscription on re-backed canvas: "Dr. Robert M. Patterson / Nat. 1787 / Ob. 1854 / Painted by Samuel F. DuBois / Jan. 1855."
Gift of Mrs. Robert Maskell Patterson, 1855.
(58.P.5)

ROBERT MASKELL PATTERSON [2] (Fig. 32)

In a letter to Dr. J. C. Morris, May 16, 1896, Dr. Patterson's son explained that his family, never entirely satisfied with the various portraits of his father, asked James Reid Lambdin to combine, with his own recollection of the subject, the virtues of all.

The portrait lodged with you by Mr. Field is the result. There is quite a difference of opinion as to Mr. Lambdin's success. My sister, Mrs. Field, her late husband, and some others who knew my father were gratified both with the likeness and the artistic merit of the portrait. The older children did not share this opinion.

By James Reid Lambdin, after other portraits and his own recollection.
Oil on canvas. $30\frac{1}{4}'' \times 25\frac{1}{8}''$.
Canvas inscribed on back: "Robert Maskell Patterson 1787–1854."
Gift of Robert Patterson Field, 1896.
(58.P.37)

CHARLES WILLSON PEALE, 1741–1827 (Fig. 23)

Artist, naturalist.
APS 1786; Librarian 1794; Curator 1788–1811.
"Peale," John Adams wrote to his wife, August 21, 1776, "is from Maryland, a tender, soft, affectionate creature. . . . He is ingenious. He has vanity, loves finery, wears a sword, gold lace, speaks French, is capable of friendship, and strong family attachments and natural affections." Peale at about the same time described himself simply as "a thin, spare, pale faced man." His little self-portrait answers both descriptions. His grandson, George Escol Sellers, recollected having seen other portraits of Revolutionary figures in the same small size, but no others have survived. They were presumably painted in camp or at the refugee home of his family during the British occupation of Philadelphia, 1777–1778. He wears in his self-portrait the brown uniform of the Philadelphia Militia and in his hat the gold braid of a Captain, the rank he held at the Battle of Princeton and in the subsequent campaigns.

Peale's election to the Society followed his determination to found a museum of natural history. The development of his

72

museum through the subsequent years was largely under the auspices of the Society and in association with it. It had a stimulating, sustaining effect upon the natural sciences in this country, with Peale himself important as a collector and pioneer in scientific exposition rather than as a scientist. In later years the museum became also a profitable popular resort, bringing wealth to its proprietor but also some attendant frictions among friends and family. Evidence of the latter was discovered in the compilation of this catalogue. In the Society's Peale Papers there is a water-color drawing of the severed head of an old man, looking as if it had just been taken from the guillotine. It may be attributed to Titian Ramsay Peale, naturalist son of the founder of the museum. The likeness is that of Charles Willson Peale.

By Charles Willson Peale, *circa* 1777–1778.
Oil on canvas. 5¾″ × 5½″.
Purchased 1951.
(58.P.67)

FRANKLIN PEALE [1], 1796–1870

Engineer inventor.
APS 1833; Curator 1838–1870.
The Minutes for February 19, 1796, record:

Mr. Peale presented to the Society a young son of four months and four days old, being the first child born in the Philosophical Hall, and requested that the Society would give him a name. On which the Society unanimously agreed that, after the name and chief founder & late President of the Society, he should be named Franklin.

During those four months and four days this one of the younger sons of Charles Willson Peale had borne the name of Aldrovand, after the early Italian naturalist who had founded a museum. The selection appears to have been too recondite for others of the family, and the Society's choice a happier one to all concerned. Early developing an interest in mechanics and engineering, Franklin Peale was associated with the United States Mint from 1833 to 1854, as Assistant Assayer, Melter and Refiner and Chief Coiner. He had an active part in the design of the coinage. Of the steam presses which he substituted for hand-operated machinery and of his other equipment, Dr. Robert Patterson said, "He brought to all the eye of an artist. It was not enough that a machine should be effective; it must also be graceful and attractive." In the years of his retirement Franklin Peale formed a fine collection of Indian artifacts (which the Society has deposited at the University Museum), served as President of the

Musical Fund Society, the Skaters' Club and the Pennsylvania Institution for the Instruction of the Deaf, founded a famous club of archers, "The United Bowmen," and was a zealous supporter of the Pennsylvania Academy of the Fine Arts.

The Society owns a print inscribed, "Engraving of Franklin Peale. Modelled by J. C. Chapman, Electrotype by Franklin Peale. Engraved with the medal ruling machine by Jos. Saxton, Mint of the United States. 1942." This identifies the artist of his bas-relief portrait.

By John Gadsby Chapman, *circa* 1842.
Plaster bas-relief. Diameter 8".
Purchased 1951.
(58.S.51)

FRANKLIN PEALE [2]

By Robert Wylie.
Plaster bust. Height 23".
Purchased 1952.
(58.S.21)

Peale's Museum. By JAMES PEALE.

In the summer of 1780 Charles Willson Peale purchased a house at the southwest corner of Third and Lombard Streets, and soon after conceived the idea of enlarging his painting-room into a portrait gallery honoring the great figures of the new republic. Two years later, November 16, 1782, the *Independent Gazette* noted, "We hear that Mr. Peale has completed his new exhibition room, which is open for the reception and entertainment of all lovers of the fine arts, being ornamented with the portraits of a great number of worthy personages." It was the first skylighted gallery in this country, and the first building erected for the exhibition of paintings. In the autumn of 1784 Peale added a skylighted room at the end to accommodate his "moving pictures," or, in the formal title which he applied to them, "Perspective Views with Changeable Effects; or, Nature Delineated, and in Motion." Two years later this dramatic entertainment was abandoned, and Peale began the collection of objects of natural history which became "The Philadelphia Museum," or more popularly "Peale's Museum," and which, in 1794, was moved into Philosophical Hall. The Third and Lombard Street House was then occupied by his brother James Peale, and it is possible that his little sketch of the place was made at that time. Rubens Peale made an enlarged and elaborated copy of it, 1858–1860, and in the register of his

74

work identified the original as by his uncle, James. There is a view of the Lombard Street house from the front in Charles Willson Peale's engraving of 1787, "The Accident in Lombard-Street."

By James Peale, circa 1784–1794.
Oil on panel. $5\frac{1}{4}'' \times 7\frac{1}{2}''$.
Purchased 1945.
(58.P.84)

WILLIAM PENN, 1644–1718

Founder of Pennsylvania.

Benjamin Franklin wrote to Lord Kames, January 3, 1760, expressing doubt as to the authenticity of a supposed portrait of William Penn. He averred that the painting should be compared closely to the only authentic likeness of Penn he knew, and cited an anecdote he had heard:

That when old Lord Cobham [Sir Richard Temple, ca. 1669–1749] was adorning his gardens at Stowe with the busts of famous men, he made inquiry of the family, for the picture of William Penn, in order to get a bust formed from it, but could find none: That Sylvanus Bevan, an old Quaker apothecary, remarkable for the notice he takes of countenances, and a knack he has of cutting in ivory strong likenesses of persons he has once seen, hearing of Lord Cobham's desire, set himself to recollect Penn's face, with which he had been well acquainted; and cut a little bust of him in ivory, which he sent to Lord Cobham, without any letter or notice that it was Penn's. But my Lord, who had personally known Penn, on seeing it, immediately cried out, "Whence comes this? It is William Penn himself!" And from this little bust, they say, the large one in the gardens was formed. (Smyth, Writings of Benjamin Franklin 4: 5–6, 1905–1907.)

From this small likeness also, presumably, the Wedgwood medallion was taken as the first and most exact reproduction of it.

By Wedgwood, nineteenth century; modeled circa 1769–1780, from the ivory bas-relief by Sylvanus Bevan.
Ceramic medallion. White on black jasper dip. $4\frac{1}{16}'' \times 3''$ (oval).
Impressed on back: "W. Penn" and "WEDGWOOD."
Provenance unknown.
(58.S.62)

RICHARD ALEXANDER FULLERTON PENROSE, JR., 1863–1931

Geologist, mining executive.
APS 1905; Councillor 1909–1912, 1913–1916.

75

The Society owns thirty-five colored sketches which accompanied Dr. Penrose's brilliant Ph.D. thesis, *The Nature and Origin of Deposits of Phosphate of Lime,* 1884, published by the United States Geological Survey. His later career was with the Survey and as a member of the faculty of the University of Chicago. During World War I he served on the National Research Council. Following his death on July 31, 1931, it was disclosed that his will, dated June 12, 1930, left the bulk of his large estate to the American Philosophical Society and the Geological Society of America in equal parts with the clause that "Both of these gifts shall be considered endowment funds, the income of which only is to be used and the capital to be properly invested." Neither institution had been aware of his intention. However, in a memorial resolution recorded in the Minutes of December 4, 1931, it was stated:

He was well acquainted with the plans of the Society for its larger usefulness to science and learning which were under discussion during all the years of his membership, and had accumulated during the past three years in the intensive campaign for increased endowment. His great bequest to the Society comes as a fitting climax to this campaign, and now makes it possible for the Society to realize some of its long-cherished plans for enlarged usefulness. This great endowment imposes upon the Society an equally great responsibility to develop a broad and useful programme that will be a great stimulus to learning and an enduring honor to the name and memory of Dr. Penrose.

By George Gibbs, 1934, from a photograph.
Oil on canvas. 40″ × 32¼″.
Signed (lower right): "George Gibbs / 34."
Painted on order, 1933–1934.
(58.P.17)

WILLIAM PEPPER, 1843–1898

Physician, medical educator.
APS 1870; Vice-President 1896–1898.

A major aim and activity of William Pepper's life was the promotion of higher standards in medical education and the strengthening of professional organization. Modern redevelopment and reorganization marked his years as Provost of the University of Pennsylvania, 1881–1894. The organization, construction and endowment of the Philadelphia Free Library is largely his work, and its "Pepper Hall" one of his most substantial memorials.

By George W. Pettit, after a photograph by Franz Meinen, 1888.
Oil on canvas. $29\frac{7}{8}'' \times 25''$.
Signed (lower left): "G. W. Pettit."
Gift of members: Daniel Baugh, George T. Bispham, Clarence
Clark, Richard A. Cleeman, John H. Converse, Charles H.
Cramp, Samuel Dickson, Ferdinand J. Dreer, George F. Ed-
munds, Theodore N. Ely, Frederick Fraley, Horace H. Furness,
I. Minis Hays, Horace Jayne, Henry Charles Lea, Francis W.
Lewis, J. Dundas Lippincott, William V. McKean, S. Weir
Mitchell, William F. Norris, C. Stuart Patterson, George Whar-
ton Pepper, Charles Platt, Joseph G. Rosengarten, Charles
Schaeffer, Coleman Sellers, A. Louden Snowden, Sara Y. Steven-
son, William Thomson, James Tyson, Isaac Wister, 1901.
(58.P.71)

HENRY MYER PHILLIPS, 1811–1884

Lawyer.
APS 1871.
A son of Zalegman Phillips, a noted criminal lawyer of Philadelphia and Parnas of the Portuguese Congregation Mikve
Israel, Henry Myer Phillips studied with his father and was admitted to the bar before the age of twenty-one. A brilliantly
endowed member of his profession, he served also as Grand
Master of the Grand Lodge of Free and Accepted Masons, 1859–
1860, and President of the Academy of Music, 1872–1884. At
the meeting of April 25, 1890, the following letter to the Society
was read:

Gentlemen:
I have the honor to offer for your acceptance, the portrait of my
brother, the late Henry M. Phillips, formerly a member of your
Society, in whose memory the Prize Essay Fund was established.
Very respectfully,
Emily Phillips

The Prize Essay Fund was for the encouragement of work in
History and the Growth of the Philosophy of Jurisprudence.
Miss Phillips also gave the Society the bas-relief of Thomas
Jefferson by George M. Miller.

By K. C. B. Neilson, probably after a photograph.
Oil on canvas. $27'' \times 22''$.
Signed: "K. C. B. N."
Gift of Miss Emily Phillips, 1890.
(58.P.63)

PHILIP SYNG PHYSICK, 1768–1837 (Fig. 28)

Physician.

APS 1802.

A Philadelphia physician, surgeon and teacher, Dr. Physick had been a student of Dr. Kuhn (a pupil of Linnaeus) in London, had taken degrees at the Royal College of Surgeons in 1791 and at Edinburgh in 1792. For many years he lectured on surgery, a branch of the profession to which through his skill and mechanical ability he had made important contributions. He published little and his influence on medical practice was largely through his students. His father had been on terms of intimate association with the Penns, and on April 6, 1838, Dr. Physick presented to the Society "the Ancient Press & Theodolite" formerly in the Penn family.

Dr. Physick's portrait bust may have come to the Society from the Athenaeum of Philadelphia (see White, William).

By William Rush, *circa* 1813.
Plaster bust. Height 24⅝".
Provenance unknown.
(58.S.6)

EDWARD CHARLES PICKERING, 1846–1919

Astronomer.

APS 1896; Vice-President 1909–1917.

Pickering graduated at the age of nineteen, *summa cum laude*, from the Lawrence Scientific School, Harvard, and from 1877 to 1919 was Director of the Harvard College Observatory. His development of photometry substituted instrumental accuracy for uncertain eye estimates. The photographic library of the Observatory is a monument—and was an innovation. He was a strong believer in cooperative research, and was an innovator in teaching physics by the experimental laboratory method. His interests embraced all sciences and extended into music and mountain climbing. Of him Joel H. Metcalf said, "To those who had the privilege of a personal acquaintance with Professor Pickering his great mind will always seem secondary to his greater heart, his generous friendship and his social charms."

By Leslie Prince Thompson, 1920, after Sarah G. Putnam, 1912.
Oil on canvas. 48⅛" × 34⅜".
Inscribed (upper right): "Copy after S. G. Putnam."
Gift of friends, 1920.
(58.P.14)

JOEL ROBERTS POINSETT, 1779–1851 (Fig. 38)

Diplomat, statesman.

APS 1827.

On September 2, 1826, Vice-President Du Ponceau wrote to Secretary John Vaughan that he had "resolved on writing to Mr. Poinsett in order to endeavor to obtain by his means some valuable Donations to the Society." In 1807–1808 Poinsett had journeyed from Saint Petersburg to Moscow to Baku on the Caspian Sea and back again. In 1810–1814 he had traveled in South America as a "special agent" of the United States, donating some objects to the Society after his return. He was then under appointment as United States Minister to Mexico. Three years later, October 15, 1829, he wrote from Mexico to the Secretary, "I am glad you have opened my collection of antiquities. . . . The second collection is ready to be sent off." The material in these gifts was exhibited at the Society, then at the Academy of Natural Sciences and is now on deposit at the University Museum. Among the botanical specimens sent by Poinsett to William Bartram was the Poinsettia, shown at the Pennsylvania Horticultural Society Exhibition in 1829.

Poinsett served as Van Buren's Secretary of War, 1837–1840, and on March 19, 1837, apropos of the Society's wish to obtain a portrait of him, he wrote to John Vaughan from Washington:

. . . The resolution of the society is highly flattering and I beg you will convey to them my most grateful acknowledgments for this testimonial of the value they attach to the contribution my situation in Mexico enabled me to make to Science. My duties here are incessant and for some time to come will confine me to this station. Mr. Sully sometimes removes from Philadelphia during the warm months, and he would find the neighborhood of this place salubrious & pleasant. If his engagements will not permit him to leave his home, I will endeavor to make my arrangements to suit his convenience; but it is impossible for me to fix the time at present. . . .

Two years later, June 26, 1839, he wrote again from Washington to Vaughan, "I saw Mr. Sully in this city a few days ago. If your Society is desirous of having their order executed he must perform the task here, for my stay in Philadelphia will be very short at any time during my continuance in office." A year later, the portrait was painted, and in the following year exhibited at the Artists Fund Society. The following letter confirms the transaction:

79

G. Ord Esq
Dear Sir
In June, of the year 1840 Mr. Vaughan paid me Two Hundred dollars for the Portrait of the Honble. J. Poinsett, which I painted at Washington.

Your friend
Thos Sully

9th Decr. 1842
The above was exclusive of the Frame, which I believe was made by Mr. Earle.

By Thomas Sully, 1840.
Oil on canvas. 30" × 24¾".
Originally signed on back: "TS 1840."
Painted on order, 1840.
(58.P.36)

ELI KIRK PRICE, 1797–1884

Lawyer, law reformer, civic leader.
APS 1844; Councillor 1866–1877; Vice-President 1877–1884.
A lawyer and politician with a pervasive and beneficent influence in Philadelphia affairs, Eli Kirk Price took a leading part in the consolidation of the city government in 1854, and the history of that reform, published in 1873, is among his varied works. He had leading roles also in the establishment of Fairmount Park, 1867, and the Centennial Exposition of 1876. He was a trustee of the University of Pennsylvania, and President of the Numismatic and Antiquarian Society. His works include, *The Trial by Jury, The Family as an Element of Government, Some Phases of Modern Philosophy, The Glacial Epochs, Sylviculture.*

Photograph enlarged and overpainted in charcoal and white chalk.
Rose-tinted paper. 29" × 25".
Gift of John Sergeant Price, 1896.
(58.P.90)

JOSEPH PRIESTLEY [1], 1733–1804

Theologian, chemist.
APS 1785.
Franklin had sponsored Priestley's election to the Royal Society of London in 1766 and, later, to the French Academy of Sciences. As the discoverer of oxygen and other gases, the

founder of the modern science of chemistry, Priestley's greatness was fully appreciated by contemporaries. When, in 1794, he sought in the United States a refuge from political persecution, the American Philosophical Society voted a special meeting in his honor, and in the year before his death honored him again with a dinner, acting, as the Minute of February 28, 1803, reads, "from their high respect for his Philosophical Labors and discoveries, and to enjoy the more particular pleasure of a social meeting."

The best-known portrait of Priestley's English years is the Wedgwood profile medallion, published in various sizes, which is related to a small Wedgwood pottery bust, now more rare. This likeness is identified as the work of Giuseppe Ceracchi by a large model signed "Ceracchi fecit" in the Wedgwood Museum at Barlaston, Stoke-on-Trent. The mercurial and roving Ceracchi had come to England in 1774, and had exhibited sculpture at the Royal Academy between 1776 and 1779. The Society's Minutes record the receipt of the four following sculptured portraits, all now unlocated, and all related to the Wedgwood version of Ceracchi:

1. In the Minutes of September 16, 1791, it is noted after the list of a donation of books, "There was presented at the same time by Mr. J. Vaughan a Profile in Plaster of Paris of Dr. Priestley particularly valuable for the Resemblance."

2. A "profile of Dr. Priestley in black leather" was presented by Dr. Robert Patterson in 1804. The New-York Historical Society owns a similar oval "impression on leather," $3\frac{1}{2}'' \times 2\frac{3}{4}''$, donated by John Pintard in 1809.

3. A plaster "bronzed bust of Dr. Priestley" was presented to the Society by J. L. Baker in 1826.

4. A "small plaster bust of Dr. Priestley" was bequeathed to the Society by John Vaughan in 1841.

The Society's large plaque of mid-nineteenth century date follows the original model but with revision of the hair and costume to conform with the "classic" character of others in the series.

By Wedgwood, *circa* 1905. By A. H. Bentley, after bust by Giuseppe Ceracchi, *circa* 1776.
Ceramic plaque. White on green jasper dip. $12'' \times 8\frac{1}{2}''$.
Inscribed in relief on the field: "PRIESTLEY." Impressed on back: "WEDGWOOD / o."
Provenance unknown.
(58.S.50)

JOSEPH PRIESTLEY [2] (Fig. 22)

On March 28, 1818, shortly after the death of Dr. Caspar Wistar, his widow wrote, "I have sent Dr. Priestley's picture to you, *to be sent in our familys name to the Philosophical Society.*" In a letter to John Vaughan she added, "I beg you as a great favor that you would spare my feelings, & do not return thanks for Dr. Priestley's picture—our ever dear Doctor did not approve of going beyond Lord Littleton's point, goodness only requisite in the female character—remember, be ye faithful."

To this the Minutes of April 3 added that it had been "long in the possession of our late president," and the *Transactions* of almost five years later that it had been "painted for our late President Caspar Wistar." A replica of this painting by Rembrandt Peale now owned by the New-York Historical Society was originally in the portrait gallery of Charles Willson Peale's Philadelphia Museum, and was included in the sale of the gallery at auction in 1854. The Society owns a catalogue of the sale in which Rembrandt Peale has checked his own works, including this one, and adding to it the date, "1801." It may be assumed that Dr. Wistar's portrait was painted at the same time.

By Rembrandt Peale, *circa* 1801.
Oil on canvas. 27½" × 22¾".
Gift of the family of Dr. Caspar Wistar, 1818.
(58.P.52)

DAVID RITTENHOUSE [1], 1732–1796 (Fig. 7)

Instrument-maker, astronomer, mathematician.

APS 1768; Secretary 1771–1772; Curator 1772–1776; Librarian, 1775; Vice-President 1780–1782, 1787–1791; Councillor 1783–1789; President 1791–1796.

His international repute as a scientist made the choice of Rittenhouse as Franklin's successor in the Presidency of the Society inevitable. His portrait, ordered by the members in the year of his election, was the second, after Franklin's, to be hung in Philosophical Hall. Its costume, an informal dressing gown, is very similar to the portrait which Charles Willson Peale had painted of Franklin in 1789 at the order of the Society but which, after learning that his earlier gift of his copy after Martin was preferred, the artist retained. It would appear from this that Peale's friends in the Society ordered the *Rittenhouse* in lieu of the *Franklin* and had suggested that the same attractive costume be used. The commission for the portrait was voted at the meeting of December 2, 1791:

82

Resolved, that Dr. Rittenhouse be requested to sit for his Portrait, and the same be painted by Mr. Peale, at the expense of the Society, to be placed in their Hall.

In 1836 the Society was asked by Draper, Toppan, Longacre & Co. to lend them the portrait in order that it could be engraved on a

new set of notes for the Bank of the U. States and Mr. Biddle is desirous of having upon them portraits of several distinguished Pennsylvanians, among others that of Rittenhouse. So it is important that the likeness should be the best that can be procured. . . .

In this, as in Peale's younger portrait of Rittenhouse, 1772, Benjamin Rush's description of his appearance is borne out. In the *Eulogium* he read at the Presbyterian Church, December 17, 1796, he said:

The countenance of Mr. Rittenhouse . . . displayed such a mixture of contemplation, benignity, and innocence, that it was easy to distinguish his person in the largest company, by a previous knowledge of his character. His manners were civil, and engaging to such a degree, that he seldom passed an hour, even in public house, in travelling through our country, without being followed by the good wishes of all who attended him.

By Charles Willson Peale, 1791.
Oil on canvas. 37⅛″ × 27″.
Painted on order, 1791.
(58.P.29)

DAVID RITTENHOUSE [2] (Fig. 8)

Always a friend to every artist-idealist, David Rittenhouse gave financial aid and encouragement to the fervent Italian Giuseppe Ceracchi, and together they visited the Pennsylvania marble quarries in a vain search for a material equal to the Italian. Ceracchi, who had been elected a member of the Society three years before, responded by presenting to it, February 6, 1795, "a bust in marble of the President." Three months later, May 15, the Minutes recorded that

Mr. Peale received permission to exhibit the Rittenhouse bust at the Exhibition of the American Academy or Columbianum on his obtaining the consent of the President.

Ceracchi, whose uncompromising zeal was largely responsible for the internal turbulence and early demise of the "Columbianum," returned to Europe soon after. He was beheaded in Paris in 1802 on a charge of conspiring to assassinate Napoleon.

The models for his *Rittenhouse* and other American busts are known to have been at Florence in 1803.

The *Rittenhouse* was exhibited at the Pennsylvania Academy of the Fine Arts in 1817, 1818, and 1819. A letter from W. Barber, engraver to the United States Mint, Philadelphia, May 15, 1871, records its use as the model for a medal honoring Rittenhouse:

The undersigned begs leave to present to the Cabinet of the American Philosophical Society, the accompanying Medal (just completed and struck) of their former President "Rittenhouse," not only as an appropriate place for it, but as a grateful return for the privilege of taking the Model from the beautiful Bust in the Society's possession. I beg leave to add that the inscription on the reverse "He belonged to the whole Human Race" is taken from the Eulogium on Rittenhouse pronounced before the Society by Dr. Benjamin Rush.

By Giuseppe Ceracchi, 1794.
Marble bust. Height 19¾".
Signed: "DE FACIE PHILADELPHIÆ / EX ECTIPO FLOREN-
    TIÆ / FACIEBAT JOS. CERACCHI / MDCCLXXXXIV."
Gift of the sculptor, 1795.
(58.S.26)

GEORGE DAVID ROSENGARTEN, 1869–1936

Chemist, pharmaceutical manufacturer.
APS 1919.
Dr. Rosengarten was associated throughout his life with the firm founded by his grandfather in 1822, Rosengarten and Sons, manufacturers of medicinal chemicals.

By Nikol Schattenstein, 1934.
Oil on canvas. 45¼" × 32¼".
Signed (lower left): "Nikol / Schattenstein / N.Y."; Inscribed on back:
    "GEORGE D. ROSENGARTEN / PINXIT AUG. 1, 1934."
Bequest of Mrs. George David Rosengarten, 1947.
(58.P.72)

JOSEPH GEORGE ROSENGARTEN, 1835–1921 (Fig. 51)

Lawyer, historian.
APS 1891; Councillor 1901–1910, 1911–1914; Vice-President 1918–1919.
After reading law in the office of Henry Myer Phillips, Joseph George Rosengarten was called to the bar in 1856. He com-

84

pleted his education at Heidelberg with studies in history and Roman law. His first work in American history, about which his later interests largely centered, was an eye-witness account of the John Brown raid, published in the *Atlantic Monthly*. Among his subsequent works were authoritative studies of French and German emigration to America. He was an effective promoter of the search in European archives for American source materials. He was active in the establishment of the Philadelphia Free Library, the historical exhibits at the Jamestown Tercentennial Exposition which did so much to promote interest in Americana, and in all of the Society's historical projects, particularly those connected with the Franklin Bicentennial.

By Julian Story, 1909.
Oil on canvas. 30″ × 25″.
Signed (upper right): "Julian Story 1909."
Gift of the subject's nieces, Mrs. George H. Saportas and Mrs. Thomas A. Dougherty, 1925.
(58.P.45)

COUNT NIKOLAY PETROVICH RUMIANTZEV, 1754–1826

APS 1825.

Going to Saint Petersburg as United States Minister in 1809, John Quincy Adams found a congenial friend in the Russian Chancellor, Minister of Foreign Affairs, and Minister of Commerce, who had a particular interest in Russian-American trade routes. On his retirement, the Count's extensive collections became the Imperial Rumiantzev Museum at Moscow, which was reorganized in 1924 and is now the Lenin State Public Library.

The Minutes of December 15, 1820, record that "Count Nicholas Romanzoff, Chancellor of the Russian Empire, presented his bust in bronze to the Society, with a letter announcing the donation." Over a year before, the Russian Consul General and Chargé d'Affaires had presented a bust of the Chancellor in plaster, bronzed. This was presumably disposed of after receipt of the second. The Chancellor was elected to membership in the Society, January 21, 1825, and his letter thanking the Society for this honor was read at the meeting, November 4.

By Theodor Ivanvitch Choubine, *circa* 1795.
Bronze bust. Height 19¼″.
Gift of Count Rumiantzev, 1820.
(58.S.27)

85

BENJAMIN RUSH, 1745-1813 (Fig. 10)

Physician, medical educator, philanthropist. Signer of the Declaration of Independence.

APS 1768; Curator 1770–1773; Secretary 1773–1776; Councillor 1786–1795, 1806–1813; Vice-President 1797–1801.

One essential character of Dr. Rush, in medicine, in government and in his various philanthropic activities, was a driving forcefulness intolerant of any opposition, and there is a curious self-revelation in the fact that he preferred to be painted as a philosopher, in an attitude of studious repose among his books. Thomas Sully's large formal portrait shows him so, as Charles Willson Peale's of many years before had done. In Sully's register of his work, as edited by Edward Biddle and Mantle Fielding (*The Life and Works of Thomas Sully*, Philadelphia, 1921), the first large portrait of Dr. Rush is the three-quarter length, recorded as No. 1528, begun May 7 and finished July 20, 1812. A replica begun September 2 and finished September 20, 1815, appears as No. 1531 and is listed by the editors as the property of the American Philosophical Society. This listing, however, does not conform with the curious history of the Society's portrait.

Thomas Sully had his studio in Philosophical Hall from 1812 to 1822. It is conjectural whether he had left in the building, or the Society later acquired in some way, an *unfinished* example of his portrait of Rush. At a Curators' meeting, held September 27, 1899, and attended by Messrs. Morris, Lyman, and Pettit, "Mr. Pettit reported the recovery of portrait of Dr. B. Rush— supposed to be study by Sully from which subsequent portraits engravings &c were made—and moved that Earle & Sons be employed to clean it & put on a stretcher, & return to the Curators. Adopted." It is not known whether the Curators' surmise that this canvas is the original, from life, was based upon traditional or written evidence, or upon the too-frequent belief that an unfinished work must be a primary "study." That the canvas is Sully's cannot be doubted, nor that artists frequently kept at hand the likeness made from life, often with background unfinished, to be used as the matrix for later replicas. From the documentation and the painting itself it is clear that the painting had been left unfinished and had at some time been folded, with considerable paint loss along the folds. The Curators asked bids for the restoration and accepted that of James T. Flaherty, described as "artist" in the Philadelphia Directory. His work, carried out at the small expenditure of $34.00, at least leaves no doubt as to which parts of the painting are Sully and which

86

Flaherty. The picture was shown before restoration at the meeting of October 6, 1899. At the meeting of December 1 it was announced that "a very valuable original portrait of Dr. Benjamin Rush, found amongst old papers &c. in the Library, is now in process of repair." Completion of the work and the return of the painting to the Hall is recorded in the Minutes of December 15.

By Thomas Sully.
Oil on canvas. $48\frac{1}{8}'' \times 38\frac{1}{8}''$.
Found in the Library, Philosophical Hall, 1899.
(58.P.51)

HENRY NORRIS RUSSELL, 1877–1957

Astronomer.

APS 1913; Vice-President 1930–1931; President 1931–1932.

At the age of twenty, Henry Norris Russell was the first recipient of Princeton's *Insignia cum Laude.* He was Director of the Princeton Observatory from 1912 until 1947. As engineer consultant in World War I his flying observations made approximately at 16,000 feet and at a speed of 105 miles per hour resulted in practical suggestions on working with different horizons and instruments for the swift reduction of observations. In World War II he was on the Ballistic Advisory Committee at the Aberdeen Proving Grounds. He saw science as a whole, and his published works embrace a wide range of subjects and are addressed to every type of public. In his *Fate and Freedom* he wrote:

When the candle is blown out, what of the flame? . . . We can blow the flame out; do we really blow out the light? Far from it; light moves in another realm, where we cannot thus extinguish it. The flame dies; but the light persists.

By Howard Russell Butler, 1933.
Oil on canvas. $39\frac{7}{8}'' \times 35\frac{7}{8}''$.
Signed (lower right): "H. R. Butler / 33."
Purchased 1937.
(58.P.22)

WILLIAM BERRYMAN SCOTT, 1858–1947 (Fig. 50)

Geologist, paleontologist.

APS 1886; Curator 1902–1903; Vice-President 1903–1918; President 1918–1925; Councillor 1929–1933.

A great-great-great-grandson of Benjamin Franklin associated with Princeton University for over seventy-four years as student and teacher, Professor Scott's works include his *Patagonian Re-*

87

ports, 1901–1932, in fifteen luxurious quartos, his *Physiography; the Science of the Abode of Man,* 1922, and his *White River Oligocene,* published by the Society, 1936–1941. In *Some Memories of a Paleontologist,* 1939, he looked back with wit and enjoyment over the years of a long and active life, recalling:

> In 1918 I received the high honor of election to the presidency of the American Philosophical Society, an office which I held with great interest and pleasure, until the statutory limitation of seven years was reached in 1925. . . . The Philosophical Society then held monthly meetings as well as the Annual General Meeting in the spring. It was my remarkable good fortune that I was never compelled, by ill health or stress of weather, to fail in attendance at a meeting, though, on one occasion, only the President and one of the Secretaries were present.

By Robert William Vonnoh, 1924.
Oil on canvas. 40⅜″ × 30⅛″.
Painted on order, 1926.
(58.P.60)

MADAME SEILER (EMMA DIRUFF), 1821–1886

Laryngologist.
APS 1870.

Emma Seiler came to Philadelphia about 1866, bringing with her from Germany her young son, Carl (1849–1905), whose distinguished career as a laryngologist was a continuance of her own. The desire of a number of her friends to present her portrait to the Society was brought to its attention by Joseph G. Rosengarten. In his presentation address, November 20, 1891, he said:

> Madame Seiler was a member of this Society, one of the six women who have thus far been enrolled on its list. . . . Her works on "The Voice in Singing" and "The Voice in Speaking" were not her only claims to this distinction. In Germany, her native country, Madame Seiler was a pupil of the famous teachers of the University of Berlin, and it is to her that is attributed the first use of the laryngoscope in studying the organs of the throat, while her discovery and description of some of the parts of the throat were of great value. . . . It was the kindness shown to her by members of the Philosophical Society that enabled her to find employment and to show her mastery of her art and to carry on her scientific work and to write her books. It is eminently fitting, therefore, that this memorial portrait should find its final resting place on the walls of your hall, and that her name and services should be perpetuated in your records.

With the portrait, Madame Seiler's laryngoscope, stated to be the first ever used in America, was also presented to the Society.

88

By Henry Kirke Bush-Brown, 1886.
Marble bas-relief. Diameter 16" (sight).
Inscribed: "1821 Emma Seiler 1886."
Gift of members and friends: Miss Bennett, Miss Bradford, Miss Mary
    A. Burnham, Miss Eliza B. Chase, Edward H. Coates, the Rev.
    Dr. T. K. Conrad, Mrs. Brinton Coxe, Mrs. John W. Field, Miss
    Kate S. Gillespie, Miss Maria Hopper, Mrs. S. I. Lesley, Mrs.
    George McClellan, Mr. and Mrs. M. H. Messchert, Miss Mess-
    chert, Miss Maria Moss, William Platt Pepper, Charles Platt,
    Miss B. M. Randolph, J. G. Rosengarten, Miss Rosengarten,
    William Ellis Scull, Mrs. Agness G. E. Shipley, Mrs. Marriott C.
    Smythe, Miss Ella C. White, Mrs. Caspar Wister, 1891.
(58.S.49)

SHAHAKA (Fig. 16)

Mandan Chief.

The friendly Mandan, Shahaka, known also as The Great
White, or Le Grand Blanc, visited the Lewis and Clark Expedition in 1804, and, with his wife and child, accompanied the
party on its return to the east. He was received at Washington
by President Jefferson on December 30, 1806, and was a guest of
honor at the dinner given to Captain Lewis, January 14, 1807,
both occasions being used to emphasize the hope for an amicable
relationship between the races. His portrait by Saint Mémin
was apparently made in Philadelphia in that year, and probably
came to the Society with the Lewis and Clark papers in 1817.
It was exhibited at the Pennsylvania Academy of the Fine Arts
in 1818, listed in the catalogue as "Portrait of Mandan, surnamed
the Great White, an Indian Chief, who accompanied Messrs.
Lewis and Clark to Philadelphia in 1807."

This drawing is the original of the lithograph in the McKenny
and Hall *History of the Indian Tribes of North America* (1: 19,
Philadelphia, 1838). The text states that its subject is the Mandan who had come east with the Lewis and Clark Expedition
and states that it had been called to the authors' attention by
John Vaughan, Librarian of the Society. An identical profile in
the collection of the New-York Historical Society bears an
inscription thought to be in Saint Mémin's hand, *"Indien
Delaware."* Saint Mémin had made a number of portraits of
Indians of different tribes at Washington in the spring of 1807,
and appears in the New-York Historical Society group, to have
been careless in his identifications. Two drawings of another Indian are variously called "Indien des Iowas des Missouri" "Mandan King." Shahaka was the only man of this tribe with the party.

By Charles Balthazar Julian Févret de Saint Mémin, 1807.
Crayon drawing on pink paper. $25\frac{1}{8}'' \times 15''$.
Inscribed: "Mandan / nomme Le Grand Blanc / venu Philada 1807 / accompagne Par M. Cheste [sic]. Lewis and Clark."
Presumably acquired with the Lewis and Clark Papers, 1817.
(58.P.35)

EDGAR FAHS SMITH, 1854–1928

Chemist, historian of science. Provost of the University of Pennsylvania.

APS 1887; President 1903–1908.

As Francis X. Dercum described Edgar Fahs Smith, "Entirely without recognition of self or of his own importance or of the great rôle that he was playing in the advance of science or in the great progress of the University under his administration, he was utterly selfless." For many years Vice-Provost and Provost of the University of Pennsylvania, he labored in that office to create a coherent and dedicated community of scholars, while at the same time making scholarly contributions of his own and of fundamental value to the history and biography of chemistry.

By Conrad Frederick Haeseler, *circa* 1915.
Oil on unidentified material. $28\frac{1}{2}'' \times 21\frac{1}{2}''$.
Signed (lower left): "CONRAD / F. HAESELER."
Gift of the artist, 1915.
(58.P.24)

THOMAS SULLY, 1783–1872 (Fig. 42)

Artist.

APS 1835.

Thomas Sully rented rooms in Philosophical Hall from 1812 until 1822, and had there not only his studio but a gallery of pictures to which the public was admitted at a charge of twenty-five cents. For the remainder of his life he occupied a house and studio built for him by Stephen Girard in order to insure his continuing to live in Philadelphia. He is now represented in the Society's collection by his self-portrait of 1867, painted for the Musical Fund Society, of which he was Vice-President, 1860–1862. Sully, a brilliant painter, was also one of the most beloved figures in the history of American art. As William Dunlap describes him in his *Rise and Progress of the Arts of Design*, 1834,

With a frame apparently slight, but in reality strong, muscular, athletic, and uncommonly active, Mr. Sully does not stand over five feet eight inches in height, but he walks with the stride of a man of six feet. His complexion is pale, hair brown, eyes grey, approaching to

90

blue, and ornamented with uncommonly long eyelashes, and his whole physiognomy marked with the wish to make others happy.

By Thomas Sully, 1867.
Oil on canvas. 30″ × 25″.
Inscribed on back: "Thomas Sully Painted / by order of the / Musical Fund / Society. / TS 1867."
Purchased 1957.
(58.P.65)

CHARLES THOMSON, 1729–1824 (Fig. 6)

Schoolmaster, statesman, Biblical scholar. Secretary of the Continental Congress.

APS 1758; Secretary 1769–1771; Councillor 1781–1782.

At the age of twenty-one, on the recommendation of Benjamin Franklin, Charles Thomson, a young immigrant from the north of Ireland, was engaged as a tutor at the Philadelphia Academy. From 1757 to 1760 he was Master of the present William Penn Charter School. In 1757, too, he was chosen by the Indians to record their proceedings in the treaty negotiations at Easton, and was adopted by them with the name, "The Man Who Tells the Truth." As the Revolution approached, he became a leader of the Whigs, forceful and adept. For nearly fifteen years he served as Secretary of the Continental Congress. Few others were so intimately and unremittingly identified with the national cause. In 1789, as a link between the old government and the new, he was chosen to give General Washington official notification of his election to the presidency. In later years he achieved a new reputation in the field of Biblical scholarship.

A bust in burnt clay of Charles Thomson by William Rush was exhibited at the Pennsylvania Academy of the Fine Arts in 1818, the owner's name unrecorded. The Society's bust may have come to it from the Athenaeum of Philadelphia (see White, William). It was for many years labeled in error "Dr. Benjamin Rush."

By William Rush, *circa* 1815.
Bust, burnt clay. Height 19¾″.
Provenance unknown.
(58.S.28)

ELIHU THOMSON, 1853–1937

Electrical engineer, inventor, manufacturer.

APS 1876; Councillor 1917–1920; Vice-President 1928–1934.

Thomson's patents number over seven hundred. He worked with x-ray and x-ray protection, and was the first in the world

91

to transmit and receive wireless impulses through masonry. His recreation was descriptive astronomy. He was one of the first in America to realize the full importance of research to industrial progress. One of his enterprises, the Thomson-Houston Company, was merged in 1892 with the Edison Company, and became the General Electric Company. From Mrs. Thomson, the General Electric Company and others the Society has received a magnificently complete collection of his papers. His wide-ranging accomplishment brought him numerous distinguished honors. Of these he wrote, March 20, 1902, to George R. Mirer:

Publicity interferes with a man's usefulness—I do not seek and never have sought it. I can say the same of honors and awards. It has been said with much truth—"When a man does anything of value attracting public notice, all the world seems to conspire to prevent his doing more of it."

By Dahl-McKenna Photographic Craftsmen.
Oil on masonite. $40\frac{1}{8}'' \times 30''$.
Signed (lower right): "Grace Dahl."
Gift of Mrs. Elihu Thomson, 1940.
(58.P.16)

WILLIAM TILGHMAN, 1756–1827 (Fig. 30)

Jurist.
APS 1805; Councillor 1806–1816; Vice-President 1816–1825; President 1825–1827.

A profound authority on the law, William Tilghman was appointed Chief Judge of the Circuit Court of the United States in 1801, and Chief Justice of the Supreme Court of Pennsylvania in 1806. His interests extended into scientific agriculture, the promotion of industry and the use of canals. He was Chairman of the Historical and Literary Committee of the American Philosophical Society, established March 17, 1815, from which emerged the organization of the Historical Society of Pennsylvania in 1824. Of him Horace Binney wrote in an obituary "Eulogium":

Not deeming it discreet to meet his fellow citizens in those assemblies where either politics or their kindred subjects were to be discussed, he seized with the more avidity, such occasions of intercourse, as were presented by meetings of public improvement, for philosophical inquiry, or the cultivation of literature; and in particular he attended with great interest to the concerns of the American Philosophical Society, of which he was chosen President, . . . and to those also of the Athenaeum, of which he was the first, and during

92

his life, its only President: the Trustees of the University of Pennsylvania rarely missed him from his seat, or the United Episcopal Churches, of this city, from their Vestry, as the Warden of his venerable friend and pastor Bishop White. It was in this way that he diminished the distance to which his office removed him from society; keeping however a constant eye upon that office even when he moved out of its orbit, and taking scrupulous care that no external contact should be of a nature to disturb his movements when he returned to it.

Immediately after Chief Justice Tilghman's death in 1827, his portrait was commissioned by a number of members. They asked Rembrandt Peale to paint a replica of his life portrait. Of his original, Charles Willson Peale had written to his son, May 22, 1819, "Your portrait of Mr. Tilghman was spoken of so highly by the family that I asked it for exhibition and it certainly does you credit. It is a fine portrait." This portrait, included in the 1819 exhibition of the Pennsylvania Academy of the Fine Arts, of which the subject was a Director, is now owned by the Academy. At the time of the Society's request it belonged to Mrs. James Greenleaf of Allentown, Chief Justice Tilghman's sister-in-law. It was not sent to Philadelphia until 1829, and then with Ann Greenleaf's cautionary warning, " of all my possessions it is the only one, which is to me invaluable."

By Rembrandt Peale, 1829, a replica of his portrait of *circa* 1819.
Oil on canvas. 30″ × 25″.
Gift of several members, 1830.
(58.P.49)

ANNE ROBERT JACQUES TURGOT, BARON D'AULNE, 1727–1781 (Fig. 5)

Economist, statesman, scientist, *litterateur*.
Twenty-five years before the event, Turgot had predicted American independence. He is perhaps best remembered by Americans for the Latin epigram with which the personal triumph of Benjamin Franklin's diplomacy is celebrated: *Eripuit coelo fulmen sceptrumque tyrannis.*
On February 17, 1810, Pierre Samuel du Pont de Nemours wrote to Turgot's nephew with the request that he permit a mold to be taken of the marble bust in his possession in order that various friends of Turgot might obtain casts. The mold retained by the artist, Jean Antoine Houdon, had been broken. In 1812 Mr. du Pont presented to the Society the edition of

93

Turgot's work which he had edited, and in 1816 added to this a cast of the bust. Of the bust he wrote, November 2, 1816:

J'ai fait venir de France le Buste de Mr. Turgot, modelé deux ans avant sa mort par le célèbre Houdon.

Mon intention a été de vous l'offrir pour le placer dans la salle de vos séances ou dans votre Bibliothèque.

Cet habile Ministre et ce grand Philosophe me parait plus convenablement dans un Edifice public et consacré aux sciences que dans l'habitation particulière d'une Famille.

Il honorarait la mienne, comme m'ont honoré ses bontés. Mais les voyageurs qui le verront a la Société philosophique, y trouveront l'occasion de parler de ses ouvrages. Il en resultera chez eux mêmes, ou chez d'autres, le dessein de les lire ou de les relire, quelques vérités utiles de plus auront été répandues et quelqu'une d'entre elles aura Porte de bons Fruits.

News of the safe receipt of the bust, with the Society's grateful acknowledgment, was returned to the donor by John Vaughan, December 23, 1816.

Houdon had exhibited a marble bust of Turgot at the Salon of 1777. The marble owned in the family, and described above as having been made two years before the subject's death, may have been the same, or a replica. The Society's cast, formerly bronzed, is now white.

By Jean Antoine Houdon, 1810, cast after his marble bust of *circa* 1777.
Plaster bust. Height 31½".
Gift of Pierre Samuel du Pont de Nemours, 1816.
(58.S.23)

JAKOB HEINRICH VAN'T HOFF, 1852–1911

Chemist, physicist.
APS 1904.

In the Society's small bronze plaque an eminent Dutch sculptor and medalist celebrates the fame of one of his country's greatest scientists. Both had followed careers which had brought them to metropolitan centers outside of the Netherlands, the artist to Rome and van't Hoff to a professorship at the University of Berlin. van't Hoff is best known for his major part in advancing the study of stereo-isomerism into the range of experimental science, and as one of the founders of stereochemistry. For this work, achieved in cooperation with J. A. Le Bel, both were awarded jointly the Davy Medal of the Royal Society in 1893.

94

By Pier Pander, *circa* 1911.
Bronze plaque, with rounded upper corners. 2 $25/32''$ × 2 $1/32''$.
Signed (lower right on shoulder): "P. Pander." Inscribed on base:
"1852 J. H. van't Hoff 1911."
Provenance unknown.
(58.S.63)

JOHN VAUGHAN [1], 1756–1841 (Fig. 21)

Librarian, merchant.

APS 1784; Secretary 1789–1791; Treasurer 1791–1841; Librarian 1803–1841.

Son of a family of English liberals who stood close to Franklin both before and after the Revolutionary conflict, John Vaughan was for half a century the voice and heart of Franklin's Philosophical Society—and spoke for his adopted city as well. President Sparks of Harvard, but one of innumerable visitors to Philadelphia who remembered and recorded the warmth and cordiality of his welcome, wrote to a friend in November, 1818:

In Philadelphia I found nothing but friends and friendly attentions. Mr. Vaughan seemed to know the moment of my arrival. He called at my lodgings very soon after I had taken them, and as I happened to be out, he left a note of the following import: You will dine at Mr. Astley's today at half-past two; in the evening you will go with me to a meeting of the Philosophical Society at their hall; tomorrow evening at 7 o'clock I shall expect you will meet the Wistar Society at my lodgings. I called on Mr. V. immediately after and found him in the character of Portuguese Consul. In addition to this he is merchant agent for Dupont's famous powder factory, librarian and most active member of the Philosophical Society, cicerone and friend to all the strangers who visit the city, occasional preacher in the Unitarian church and parish minister to all the poor of that society, . . . recommender-general of all schoolmasters, inventors, young men just entering their professions, and every sort of personage, whose characters are good, and who can be benefited by his aid. . . .

Mr. Vaughan, in the plenitude of his goodness, proposed a mathematical breakfast at his lodgings. . . . We met, therefore, at 7 o'clock, two hours before anybody else was up, and this because Mr. V. is always engaged at 9. I found among others Prof. Patterson. . . . Dr. Jones, the chemist, made another of the party. But his head was so full of steam engines that there was no room for algebra or diagrams. I had already the night before had the pleasure of being at tea, with Mr. Whitney, a Welsh mathematical instrument maker, and protege of Mr. V., with some newly contrived instruments for my inspection. . . . I was at a society, or at a dinner, or at a tea every day and almost every hour. But I was almost wholly among scientific men and artists. . . . I was several times in company with LeSueur, the famous

95

French artist. . . . I also had a long conversation with Mr. DuPonceau, who studies all languages. . . . (H. B. Adams, *Jared Sparks,* 133–134, 1893.)

The Society, at the meeting of June 20, 1823.

Resolved, that the librarian, Mr. John Vaughan, on consideration of his extraordinary care and attention to the library, for his great exertions in procuring contributions for it and for his own, very liberal donations, receive the special thanks of the Society, and Re-solved, that he be requested to sit for his portrait to be executed at the expense of the Society, and preserved in their Hall, as a token of the sense which they entertain of his merits and services. Unanimously adopted.

Thomas Sully's portrait was inspected at the meeting of October 3, 1823, and an appropriation of $100.00 authorized in payment. The portrait, of which Sully probably made more than one replica, was engraved with the following inscription: "JOHN VAUGHAN ESQ. / Engraved by J. W. Steel from the original painted by Sully for the American Philosophical Society, W. Duffee Printer. Copy right secured. Published by R. H. Hobson 147 Chestnut Street Philada." There is also a lithograph by Herline and Hensel, Philadelphia, with the figure in reverse and a facsimile signature. In 1839, perhaps referring to one of the prints, William Vaughan wrote from London that friends thought "your likeness was a very good one."

By Thomas Sully, 1823.
Oil on canvas. 30″ × 25″.
Painted on order, 1823.
(58.P.43)

JOHN VAUGHAN [2]

On October 21, 1842, Jacob Snider, Jr., John Vaughan's business associate and his principal heir, wrote to the Society:

I have the honor to request the Society's acceptance of a Bust of their late fellow member, Mr. John Vaughan, which I have caused to be delivered to the Society's room.

Should the Society decide to place it in a situation similar to the Bust of Mr. William Vaughan, I should be happy, if permitted, to furnish a similar Gilt Bracket for the Present Bust.

By Ferdinand Pettrich, 1842.
Plaster bust. Height 26¼″.
Cut in back: "John Vaughan / original bust / F Pettrick Aug. 1842."
Gift of Jacob Snider, Jr., 1842.
(58.S.19)

96

SAMUEL VAUGHAN, 1720–1802 (Fig. 20)

Merchant, philanthropist.
APS 1784; Vice-President 1785–1787.

"As to our connections," Samuel Vaughan had written from London, to Benjamin Franklin at Paris, April 28, 1778, "they are rank Whig and American." The firm of Samuel Vaughan and Sons had both American connections and a strong liberal bias. Mr. Vaughan himself came to Philadelphia on the conclusion of the peace in 1783, and remained until 1790. Benjamin Rush wrote in 1786 of the city's "great obligations to him:"

We look forward with pain to the time of his leaving us. He has been the principal cause of the resurrection of our Philosophical Society. He has done even more, he has laid the foundation of a philosophical *hall* which will preserve his name and the name of his family among us for many, many years to come.

At the same time, he had the State House Yard laid out as a garden with serpentine walks, mounds, and depressions, and groves of trees and shrubbery in which he sought to have represented all the American varieties. At the news of his death Charles Willson Peale wrote to Jefferson,

The trees in the State-House-Garden are in mourning with fallen leaves . . .—their founder, Mr. Vaughan, Senr has departed this life! Philosophical Hall would not have been reared but through the Industry & perseverence [of] the good old man!

Samuel Vaughan had encouraged the English artist, Robert Edge Pine, to emigrate to America in 1784. Pine's portrait of Vaughan, which is very much in his English manner, was probably begun soon after his arrival, and completed with the addition of the still life in 1787. His subject is shown reading the "Constiution of the United States of America," with volumes of "Locke," "Price," "English Politics" and "American Phil trans" stacked before him. At the right is a bas-relief profile of Franklin probably painted from the Houdon bust, and at the left a corner of Philosophical Hall and a tree to represent its attendant garden.

John Vaughan exhibited the portrait at the Pennsylvania Academy of the Fine Arts, 1837, as the work of Pine. In 1841 he bequeathed it to the Society as "the portrait of my late father, Samuel Vaughan, in which are introduced the garden which he improved and the building of the Society for which the lot was chiefly procured and the building constructed through his means." For some years it was listed as a portrait of Francis

97

Hopkinson by Charles Willson Peale, an error which was corrected by Charles Henry Hart (*Proc. Amer. Philos. Soc.* **25:** 292, 1892). In 1790 a copy of the portrait had been made by Charles Peale Polk for Benjamin Vaughan of Hallowell, Maine.

By Robert Edge Pine, *circa* 1785–1787.
Oil on canvas. $36\frac{1}{8}'' \times 29''$.
Bequest of John Vaughan, 1841.
(58.P.3)

WILLIAM VAUGHAN, 1752–1850

Merchant, writer on navigation and docks.
APS 1830.

William Vaughan, a figure of importance in the mercantile and shipping world of London, maintained, as his brother, John, was doing in Philadelphia, the liberal and intellectual heritage of his family, a heritage derived also in part from his father's friendship with Benjamin Franklin. The portrait of Franklin which hung in his house, a work of Joseph Wright, came after his death to Philadelphia and is now owned by the Pennsylvania Academy of the Fine Arts. A bust of William Vaughan was made in 1811 by Sir Francis Chantrey. A lithograph after it is inscribed:

WILLIAN VAUGHAN, ESQUIRE / Drawn by the Revd. Daniel Alexander M.A. and on Stone by R. J. Lane A.R.A. 1839 / From a bust by Sir Francis Chantrey—1811 / in the possession of Daniel Alexander Esqre. / J Graft Printer to Her Majesty.

A cast of this bust was presented to the Society by Jacob Snider, Jr., John Vaughan's principal heir and former business associate. His accompanying letter to the Secretaries is dated Philadelphia, January 21, 1842:

I desire to present to the American Philosophical Society the copy owned by the late Mr. Vaughan of Chantrys Bust of William Vaughan of London, his Brother. . . .

Cast after bust by Sir Francis Legatt Chantrey, 1811.
Plaster bust. Height $24\frac{1}{2}''$.
Gift of Jacob Snider, Jr., 1842.
(58.S.10)

ROBERT WALSH, 1784–1859

Journalist, editor, publisher.
APS 1812; Secretary 1819–1827; Councillor, 1827–1830.

Trained in the law, widely traveled and experienced, Robert Walsh's career became centered in literature. He founded, owned, edited, and contributed to American magazines, wrote biographies and political essays. Edgar Allen Poe praised his style and Henry Wheaton, the historian wrote from Copenhagen:

I am rejoiced to see that Mr. Walsh's periodical is so skillfully conducted, and that it is *American from tip to toe*. It was nothing more than I expected, but still gladdens my heart to see it laying on the tables of the Athenaeum here without fear alongside of its English, French and German contemporaries.

After 1837 he lived at Paris, writing for French journals, acting as correspondent for New York and Washington newspapers, and serving as United States Consul-General.

By unidentified artist after Thomas Sully's portrait of 1814.
Miniature on ivory. $4\frac{5}{8}'' \times 3\frac{5}{8}''$.
Purchased 1951.
(58.P.75)

GEORGE WASHINGTON [1], 1732–1799 (Fig. 12)

Soldier, planter. First President of the United States.
APS 1780.

At a special meeting of the Society, December 27, 1799, in response to the news of the death of Washington, it was voted that the members should wear mourning for thirty days, and "Agreed that a Portrait of George Washington be procured to be hung in the Society's Hall." In conformity with this resolution, a portrait by Gilbert Stuart was presented for inspection at the meeting of April 1, 1803. On April 15 the matter was referred to a committee consisting of Mr. W. Hamilton, Mr. Latrobe, and Dr. Jacobs. On May 20, the Committee reported:

That the Portrait is equal if not superior to other copies of the bust of Mr. Stuarts whole length portrait of General Washington, made by himself, which your committee have seen. The picture possesses the strong likeness and spirit of the original; and it having been painted about 6 years ago the present state of the coloring proves that more than usual attention has been paid to the goodness and durability of the colours which have been used.

The commendation of your committee can add nothing to the acknowledged merit of Mr. Stuart's performances nor is it necessary to remark on the peculiarities in the drawing in this individual portrait,—for they are those which the original possesses.

The price of the portrait as it includes the frame, is below that of other portraits of the same kind, but the amount of the value of the frame which may be about 16 Dollars.

Upon the whole, as it is now impossible to obtain an *original* portrait of this illustrious Member of the American Philosophical

99

Society, your Committee are of opinion, that it is not probable that a wish of the Society to possess his likeness will ever be better fulfilled than by the acquisition of that now offered.

This is the only Stuart replica of Washington owned today by an organization which purchased it from the artist.

By Gilbert Stuart, *circa* 1797.
Oil on canvas. $29\frac{3}{16}'' \times 24\frac{1}{4}''$.
On order, 1799. Purchased from the artist, 1803.
(58.P.25)

GEORGE WASHINGTON [2]

The State of Virginia, at the close of the Revolutionary War, voted to erect a statue of Washington. Jefferson and Franklin joined in the arrangements by which the French sculptor, Jean Antoine Houdon, was brought to America for the purpose. Franklin, whose return voyage from France had been made with the artist as a fellow passenger, wrote to Washington from Philadelphia, September 20, 1785, that Houdon was on his way to Mount Vernon, and Washington, in a diary note of October 2, noted:

Mr. Houdon, sent from Paris by Doctr. Franklin and Mr. Jefferson to take my Bust, in behalf of the State of Virginia, with three young man assistants . . . arrived here.

And on the seventh:

Sat today as I had done yesterday, for Mr. Houdon to form my Bust.

Charles Thomson wrote to Jefferson on November 2:

Mr. Houdon has been to Mount Vernon and taken the bust of our amiable General. *He exhibited it to the view of Congress.* It appears to me to be executed in a masterly manner. I acknowledge my want of skill to judge of performance of this nature, but there is in the air and attitude of this, something that pleases me. Most other pictures seem to have their attention turned on the objects around them, but in this the artist, by elevating the chin and countenance, has given it the air of one looking forward into futurity.

Cast after Jean Antoine Houdon's bust of 1785.
Plaster bust. Height $25\frac{1}{2}''$.
Gift of Thomas Fletcher, 1830.
(58.S.11)

100

GEORGE WASHINGTON [3]

By Wedgwood, nineteenth century. From the medal by Pierre Simon
Benjamin Duvivier, based on Jean Antoine Houdon's bust sculp-
tured from life in 1785.
Ceramic medallion. White on black jasper dip. $7'' \times 6''$ (oval).
Impressed on back: "Washington" and "WEDGWOOD."
Provenance unknown.
(58.S.41)

ARTHUR WELLESLEY, DUKE OF WELLINGTON, 1769–1852

Soldier, statesman.

When, or by whose agency, or for what reason the bust of the
"Iron Duke" came to the Society is not known. It has, however,
for so long a time looked down upon the readers in the Library
that the years have come to justify its presence there, and the
bland hauteur of the conqueror of Napoleon imperceptably but
finally become an element of that studious atmosphere.

Cast after a bust by Sebastian Gahagan.
Plaster bust. Height $26\frac{1}{4}''$.
Provenance unknown.
(58.S.20)

WILLIAM WHITE, 1748–1836 (Fig. 9)

First Protestant Episcopal Bishop of Pennsylvania.

APS 1768; Secretary 1779–1783; Vice-President 1783–1790;
Councillor 1792–1798, 1804–1819.

William White arrived in London from Philadelphia in 1770,
bringing a letter of introduction from Mrs. Franklin to her
husband. "As worthy a young Jentelman as ever wente over to
Ingland," Deborah had written, an estimate of his character
which William White's long career as a churchman was fully to
justify.

In the 1814 exhibition of the Pennsylvania Academy of the
Fine Arts, George M. Miller exhibited a "Bust of the Rt. Rev.
Bishop White the original model. For Sale." From Philadelphia,
November 10, 1814, Miller wrote as follows to the Managers
of the Athenaeum of Philadelphia:

Gentlemen

I do myself the honor of depositing in the Athenaeum under your
control, the following Casts, *vizt.* Washington, Franklin, Bishop
White, Shakespere, Venus De Medici, the Empresses Ottavia, &

101

Valerie, two Antique Funeral Urns, a small wholelength figure of Antinous, small Busts, of Susanna, & Adonis.

The three first of the Busts are bronzed, the others waxed, the urns varnished. They will bear Washing with pure water and a spunge.

You will please to suffer the Enclosed Notice to be affixed under the Bust of Washington. I remain Respectfully

   your Obedient Humble Servant
     George M. Miller
     Modeller, Walnut—2 Doors above 5 Street.

The Order Book of the Athenaeum records the payment of $50.00, May 15, 1820, "for Busts deposited by G. Miller." There is no entry on the number or subjects of the busts purchased, but it is probable that the entire group is included, and that all of these busts adorned the rooms in Philosophical Hall which the Athenaeum occupied for nearly thirty years, from April, 1818, until October, 1847. It is a reasonable inference that at its removal to its new building on Washington Square the busts of members of the Society in its possession, the *White* and possibly the *Franklin* mentioned in Miller's letter, were left behind. The *Shakespeare* and a *Milton* by Miller but not mentioned in his letter, were included in the removal, and may have been considered the only ones appropriate to a general library. Since the Society's *Philip Syng Physick, Charles Thomson* and a duplicate *Caspar Wistar,* all by William Rush, have no recorded provenance, and busts of them had been owned by the Athenaeum, it is possible that these also were permitted to remain at Philosophical Hall by a similar decision. The empresses, "Ottavia" and "Valerie," abandoned by the Athenaeum, have remained, on suffrance, in the attic of Philosophical Hall.

George M. Miller died in 1819, and a cast of his *William White* was exhibited at the Academy by his widow in 1821. The Society's bust was for many years wrongly identified as "William Smith," an error which, in ignorance of a letter of correction from Charles Henry Hart, December 8, 1896, persisted until the compilation of the present catalogue.

By George M. Miller, *circa* 1814.
Plaster bust. Height 25½".
Signed (on back above base): "Made by / G. M. Miller."
Probably acquired from the Athenaeum of Philadelphia, 1847.
(58.S.12)

ALEXANDER WILSON, 1766-1813 (Fig. 35)

Ornithologist.

APS 1813.

Wilson, poet and naturalist, came from Scotland to Philadelphia in 1794. His monument is his nine-volume *American Ornithology, or Birds of the United States*. It is a monument as well to the circle of friends who encouraged the long labor. The Peale collection of birds contributed to it. From William Bartram he had caught what he called "that Itch for Drawing." The last two volumes appeared after his death, one edited and one written by George Ord.

A stipple engraving by David Edwin after the Society's portrait was published in the *Port Folio* of 1814, with the inscription, "Peale Pinxit. D. Edwin Sc." The Minutes of June 21, 1822, record the gift to the Society by Dr. Nathaniel Chapman of "the original portrait of Alexander Wilson, the American Ornithologist, presented to him by S. Brandford."

By Rembrandt Peale, *circa* 1809-1813.
Oil on panel. $20\frac{1}{4}'' \times 16\frac{11}{16}''$.
Gift of Dr. Nathaniel Chapman, 1822.
(58.P.31)

JAMES WILSON, 1742-1798

Jurist, statesman. Signer of the Declaration of Independence.
APS 1768; Vice-President 1781-1783.

James Wilson arrived in Philadelphia from Scotland in the midst of the Stamp Act agitation, was admitted to the Philadelphia Bar in the next year. His widely-read *Considerations on the Nature of the Legislative Authority of the British Parliament* was published in 1774. He signed both the Declaration of Independence and the Constitution of the United States. In 1789 he was appointed to the bench of the Pennsylvania Supreme Court, and in that year instituted a course in law at the College of Philadelphia, his opening lecture attended by President Washington and other federal and state officials.

All portraits of Wilson are derived from a single original, a miniature now attributed to Henry Pelham and owned by the National Collection of Fine Arts, Smithsonian Institution.

By Henry B. McIntyre, 1937, after a copy from the miniature attributed to Henry Pelham.
Oil on canvas. $30'' \times 25''$.
Signed (lower left): "H. B. McIntyre 1937."
Purchased 1938.
(58.P.69)

103

WOODROW WILSON, 1856–1924

Educator, historian, statesman. Twenty-eighth President of the United States.
APS 1897.

Relief, perhaps enlarged after George W. Morgan's second inauguration medal, 1917.
Bronzed metal bas-relief. Diameter $9\frac{3}{4}''$.
Purchased 1924.
(58.S.40)

CASPAR WISTAR [1], 1761–1818

Physician, anatomist.
APS 1787; Curator 1792–1795; Vice-President 1795–1815; President 1815–1818.

Wistar's *System of Anatomy* of 1811, the first American text on the subject, is today not so well remembered as the charm and sophistication of a life which extended beyond his profession into humanities and social intercourse. The Society's Historical and Literary Committee, organized March 17, 1815, became a major interest. Weekly gatherings at his house over a period of many years became a feature of Philadelphia life with which the Society was intimately connected, and which are continued as the Wistar Association today. The vine *Wistaria* was so named in his honor by Nuttall in the year of his death. Chief Justice Tilghman, in an obituary address, gives a glimpse of the Doctor's appearance and manner:

Even his person gave evidence of philanthropy—his eye beamed good will, and his whole air brought strongly to my mind what Tacitus says, in his description of Agricola: "At first sight you would have believed him good, and wished him to be great." This ruling sentiment threw grace over his actions, and inspired his conversation with a charm. He never assumed—never displayed his own superiority. On the contrary, he led the conversation to subjects in which others excelled. The pedantry of technical language he despised, and listened, with patience and politeness, to observations of inferior understanding.

At the meeting of April 3, 1818, the Society appointed Messrs. Vaughan, Morgan, and Collins a committee to seek to procure a portrait of the late President. Much later, on July 22, 1830, President Du Ponceau wrote to Mrs. Mifflin Wistar, asking the loan of the portrait owned by her, in order that a copy might be made for the Society by Thomas Sully. This was accordingly done, the copy being recorded by Sully as completed in 1830.

104

On January 7, 1831, Henry Seybert wrote to the President and members requesting the honor of presenting it, "Having always entertained great respect and veneration for Dr. Wistar & his memory being particularly endeared to me from the circumstances of the most intimate friendship which long subsisted between him & my Father."

By Thomas Sully, 1830, after a portrait by Bass Otis, 1817.
Oil on canvas. 30" × 25⅛".
Gift of Henry Seybert, 1831.
(58.P.26)

CASPAR WISTAR [2] (Fig. 24)

The 1813 catalogue of the exhibition at the Pennsylvania Academy of the Fine Arts lists a bust of Dr. Wistar by William Rush, "modelled in clay, burnt." In the association between artist and subject there was something more than warm friendship, since between 1808 and 1820 the Doctor had employed Rush to make large anatomical models in wood for teaching purposes. They are still in use today at the Medical School of the University of Pennsylvania. In 1818, the year of the Doctor's death, John Vaughan gave the Society busts of Caspar Wistar and of Alexander Hamilton. In 1896 the Society presented duplicate busts of Wistar and of Franklin to the Wistar Institute. The possession of these duplicates can be explained by the assumption that the Society received a group of busts of members from the Athenaeum of Philadelphia in 1847 (see White, William).

By William Rush, *circa* 1813.
Plaster bust. Height 25½".
Cast in back: "CASPAR WISTAR."
Probably gift of John Vaughan, 1818.
(58.S.9)

ISAAC JONES WISTAR, 1827–1905

Lawyer, soldier, philanthropist.
APS 1893; Councillor 1896–1898, 1903–1905; Vice-President 1899–1903; President 1902–1903.
A "Forty-niner" who had studied for the bar and established a law practice in San Francisco, Isaac Jones Wistar returned East and at the outbreak of the Civil War raised and led the "California Regiment" (later the 71st Pennsylvania). In 1892 his benefactions created the Wistar Institute of Anatomy and

105

Biology whose research and publications continue the work begun by his great-uncle, Dr. Caspar Wistar.

A letter from Henry M. Howe to I. Minis Hays, July 3, 1906, records that Mr. Uhle had finished the copy of the portrait of General Wistar which he was making for the Society, and that payment would be made as soon as the other members concerned had expressed their satisfaction.

By Bernard Uhle, 1906, after his painting of 1888.
Oil on canvas. 30″ × 25″.
Inscribed on back: "General I. J. Wistar, at the age of 59. / B. Uhle pinxt."
Gift of subscribing members, 1906.
(58.P.42)

GEORGE BACON WOOD [1], 1797–1879

Physician, pharmacologist.
APS 1829; President 1859–1879.

Dr. Wood was Professor of Chemistry and then of Materia Medica at the Philadelphia College of Pharmacy, 1822–1835. He was on the faculty of the University of Pennsylvania, 1835–1860 as Professor of Materia Medica and Pharmacy, and Professor of the Theory and Practice of Medicine. With Dr. Franklin Bache he compiled the *Dispensatory of the United States,* published in 1833. Among his other works was his *Practice of Medicine* of 1847, a text which had wide circulation in the United States and Great Britain. From 1850 to 1860 he was Chairman of the national committee for the revision of the *United States Pharmocopeia.* In 1860, the year of his retirement from active practice, he set out on an extensive foreign tour. One of the smaller of his many benefactions to the Society and other institutions was the marble bust of Franklin by Menconi.

At the meeting of May 7, 1880, the "President suggested the desirability of the Society's now placing on its walls a portrait of Dr. Wood, deceased, the late President of the Society." The Minutes of July 21, 1882, record that "The copy of Dr. G. B. Wood's portrait in the University, by Miss M. W. Lesley, ordered by the Society, was exhibited."

By Margaret Lesley Bush-Brown, *circa* 1882, after Samuel B. Waugh, 1859.
Oil on canvas. 35⅞″ × 29 1/16.
Painted on order, 1880–1882.
(58.P.50)

106

GEORGE BACON WOOD [2] (Fig. 40)

A bust of Dr. Wood, by Edward Stauch, was exhibited at the Pennsylvania Academy of the Fine Arts in 1857 as the property of J. B. Lippincott.

Attributed to Edward Stauch, *circa* 1857.
Marble bust. Height 27″.
Bequest of Walter Wood, 1935.
(58.S.31)

UNKNOWN MAN (Fig. 55)

Long listed in error as a bust of Simeon DeWitt (*q.v.*).

By unidentified artist.
Plaster bust. Height 26½″.
Cut in support: "Dewitt."
Provenance unknown.
(58.S.13)

Index of Artists

Original artists, copyists, and restorers are listed without distinction

Ezra Ames, 1768–1836
  Eclipse of June 16, 1806.
Thomas Pollock Anshutz, 1851–1912
  Isaac Lea. Fig. 39.
Anna Margaretta Archambault, 1856–1956
  Herman Haupt
François, Marquis de Barbé-Marbois, 1745–1837
  The American Union. Fig. 59.
A. H. Bentley (Bert Bentley), ac. 1891–1936
  Sir Joseph Banks
  Robert Boyle
  Charles Robert Darwin
  Benjamin Franklin [33]
  Isaac Newton [4]
  Joseph Priestley [1]
Sylvanus Bevan
  William Penn
Thomas Birch, 1779–1851
  Benjamin Franklin [1]. Fig. 1.
  Fairmount Water Works. Fig. 57.
Hugh Henry Breckenridge, 1870–1937
  Henry Charles Lea
Frédéric Brou, 1862–1926
  Benjamin Franklin [34, 35]
John Brown, 1752–1787
  John Napier
David Stewart Erskine, Earl of Buchan, 1742–1829
  Nicolas Copernicus
Cameron Burnside, 1887–1952
  Edwin Grant Conklin. Fig. 52.
  Roland Sletor Morris. Fig. 53.
Henry Kirke Bush-Brown, 1857–1935
  Madame Seiler
Margaret Lesley Bush-Brown (Mrs. Henry Kirke Bush-Brown), 1857–1944
  Frederick Fraley. Fig. 44.
  J. Peter Lesley
  George Bacon Wood [1]
Howard Russell Butler, 1856–1934
  Henry Norris Russell

108

Jean Jacques Caffiéri, 1725–1792
Benjamin Franklin [10, 12, 13, 14]. Fig. 3.
Pietro Cardelli, ac. 1818
John Quincy Adams [1]. Fig. 36.
Carrier-Belleuse (Carrier de Belleuse), Albert Ernest, 1824–1887
Benjamin Franklin [22]
Giuseppe Ceracchi, 1751–1802
Alexander Hamilton [1, 2]. Fig. 17.
Joseph Priestley [1]
David Rittenhouse [2]. Fig. 8.
Mason Chamberlin, ac. 1760–1787
Benjamin Franklin [6]
Sir Francis Legatt Chantrey, 1781–1841
William Vaughan
John Gadsby Chapman, 1808–1889
Franklin Peale [1]
Theodor Ivanvitch Choubine (Schubin), 1740–1805
Nikolay Petrovich Rumiantzev
Charles Nicolas Cochin, 1715–1790
Benjamin Franklin [3, 25]
Katherine M. Cohen, 1859–1914
Albert Abraham Michelson
Margaretta P. Cope
Benjamin Franklin [9]
Grace Dahl
Elihu Thomson
I. Dassier et Fils
John Paul Jones
Pierre Jean David d'Angers, 1788–1856
Georges Cuvier
Alice De Haven
Thomas Dunlap
Herman F. Deigendesch, 1858–1921
Thomas Hopkinson
Samuel F. DuBois, 1805–1889
Robert Maskell Patterson [1]
Joseph Siffred Duplessis, 1725–1802
Benjamin Franklin [4, 7, 8, 9]
Augustin Dupré, 1748–1833
John Paul Jones
Pierre Eugène Du Simitière, *ca.* 1736–1784
John Jay
Pierre Simon Benjamin Duvivier, 1728–1819
George Washington [3]
Thomas Eakins, 1844–1916
Daniel Garrison Brinton. Fig. 47.
Henry Jackson Ellicott, 1848–1901
George Walter Melville

109

Robert Feke, ac. 1741–1750
  Thomas Hopkinson
Fiorelli
  Peter Stephen Du Ponceau [2]
James T. Flaherty, ac. 1899
  Benjamin Rush. Fig. 10.
John Flaxman, 1755–1826
  Sir Joseph Banks
  Benjamin Franklin [15]. Fig. 4.
  William Franklin
  William Temple Franklin
Sebastian Gahagan, ac. 1800–1835
  Duke of Wellington
George Gibbs, 1870–1942
  Francis Xavier Dercum
  Richard Alexander Fullerton Penrose, Jr.
Isaac Gosset, 1713–1799
  Benjamin Franklin [27, 28]
William Hackwood, ?–1836
  Benjamin Franklin [33]
  Erasmus Darwin
Conrad Frederick Haeseler
  Edgar Fahs Smith
George Peter Alexander Healy, 1813–1894
  Benjamin Franklin [5]. Fig. 56.
Thomas Hicks, 1823–1890
  John Kintzing Kane. Fig. 37.
Hoskins and Grant, ac. 1775–1809
  Robert Boyle
  Isaac Newton [4]
Jean Antoine Houdon, 1741–1828
  Marquis de Condorcet. Fig. 11.
  Benjamin Franklin [11, 15, 16]. Fig. 4.
  Thomas Jefferson [1]. Fig. 14.
  Anne Robert Jacques Turgot. Fig. 5.
  George Washington [2, 3]
Robert Ball Hughes, 1806–1868
  Nathaniel Bowditch. Fig. 33.
Daniel Huntington, 1816–1906
  Louis Jean Rodolphe Agassiz. Fig. 45.
  Alexander Dallas Bache. Fig. 41.
Lewis Iselin, Jr., 1913–
  Benjamin Franklin [12]
James Reid Lambdin, 1807–1889
  Baron von Humboldt. Fig. 29.
  Elisha Kent Kane [1]
  Robert Maskell Patterson [2]. Fig. 32.
J. Lanelli,
  Alexander Hamilton [2]. Fig. 17.

110

Charles B. Lawrence, ac. 1813–1837
  José Francesco Correa da Serra. Fig. 34.
Francesco Lazzarini, ac. 1792
  Benjamin Franklin [12]
Jean Jacques François Lebarbier, 1738–1826
  Benjamin Franklin [11]
John Charles Lochee, ac. 1772–1790
  William Temple Franklin
James Barton Longacre, 1794–1869
  Zaccheus Collins
Harold L. MacDonald, 1861–
  Simon Newcomb
Henry B. McIntyre, 1872–
  James Wilson
Robert Tait McKenzie, 1867–1938
  Henry Herbert Donaldson
  Guglielmo Ferrero
  Henry LaBarre Jayne
Marbois. *See Barbé-Marbois*
David Martin, 1737–1798
  Benjamin Franklin [1]. Fig. 1.
Domenico Menconi
  Benjamin Franklin [16]
George M. Miller, ?–1819
  Thomas Jefferson [2]. Fig. 15.
  William White. Fig. 9.
Giulio Monteverde, 1837–1917
  The Genius of Franklin. Fig. 58.
George W. Morgan
  Woodrow Wilson
Samuel Murray, 1870–1941
  George Walter Melville
John Neagle, 1796–1865
  Mathew Carey
  George Ord
K. C. B. Neilson
  Henry Myer Phillips
Jean Baptiste Nini, 1718–1786
  Benjamin Franklin [29–33]
Bass Otis, 1784–1861
  Caspar Wistar [1]
Pier Pander, 1864–1919
  Jakob Heinrich van't Hoff
Thomas Park (Parke), ac. 1759–1834
  Nicolas Copernicus
Charles Willson Peale, 1741–1827
  Benjamin Franklin [1]. Fig. 1.

Charles Willson Peale (*continued*)
  Charles Willson Peale. Fig. 23.
  David Rittenhouse [1]. Fig. 7.
James Peale, 1749–1831
  Benjamin Franklin [1]. Fig. 1.
  Peale's Museum.
"Patrick Peale," ac. 1823
  J. G. E. Heckewelder. Fig. 27.
Rembrandt Peale, 1778–1860
  Jean Baptiste Joseph Delambre
  François André Michaux
  Robert Patterson. Fig. 19.
  Joseph Priestley [2]. Fig. 22.
  William Tilghman. Fig. 30.
  Alexander Wilson. Fig. 35.
Henry Pelham, 1749–1806
  James Wilson
E. Luigi Persico, 1791–1860
  Nicholas Biddle
  Nathaniel Chapman [1]
  John Bannister Gibson
  Marquis de Lafayette [4]. Fig. 18.
George W. Pettit, ?–1910
  Edward Drinker Cope
  William Pepper
Ferdinand Pettrich (Frederick August Ferdinand Pettrich), 1798–1872
  John Vaughan [2]
Robert Edge Pine, *ca.* 1730–1788
  Samuel Vaughan. Fig. 20.
Sarah G. Putnam, ac. 1900
  Edward Charles Pickering
Lazar Raditz, 1887–
  Isaac Minis Hays. Fig. 49.
  Samuel Pierpont Langley
Peter Reniers, ac. 1857
  Elisha Kent Kane [2]. Fig. 46.
Louis François Roubiliac, *ca.* 1705–1762
  Isaac Newton [3, 4]
William Rush, 1756–1833
  Philip Syng Physick. Fig. 28.
  Charles Thomson. Fig. 6.
  Caspar Wistar [2]. Fig. 24.
Charles Balthasar Julien Févret de Saint Mémin, 1770–1852
  Shahaka. Fig. 16.
Augustin de Saint Aubin
  Benjamin Franklin [3]
Nikol Schattenstein, 1877–
  George David Rosengarten

112

Gustav Anton von Seckendorf, ac. 1823
 J. G. E. Heckewelder. Fig. 27.
J. Henry Smith, ac. 1894
 George Ord
T. Henry Smith, ac. 1844
 Mathew Carey
Staffordshire pottery
 Benjamin Franklin [20, 21, 26]
Edward Stauch, ac. 1850–1860
 George Bacon Wood [2]. Fig. 40.
Alice Kent Stoddard
 Thomas Sovereign Gates. Fig. 54.
Julian Story, 1857–1919
 Joseph George Rosengarten. Fig. 51.
Gilbert Stuart, 1755–1828
 George Washington [1]. Fig. 12.
Thomas Sully, 1783–1872
 Nathaniel Chapman [2]. Fig. 31.
 Peter Stephen Du Ponceau [1]. Fig. 26.
 Thomas Jefferson [3]. Fig. 13.
 Joel Roberts Poinsett. Fig. 38.
 Benjamin Rush. Fig. 10.
 Thomas Sully. Fig. 42.
 John Vaughan [1]. Fig. 21.
 Robert Walsh
 Caspar Wistar [1]
François Marie Suzanne, ac. 1750–1802
 Benjamin Franklin [17–22]
James Tassie, 1735–1799
 Earl of Buchan
Leslie Prince Thompson, 1880–
 Edward Charles Pickering
Bernard Uhle (Albrecht Bernhard Uhle), 1847–1929
 Isaac Lea. Fig. 39.
 Joseph Leidy [2]
 Isaac Jones Wistar
Henry Ulke, 1821–1910
 Spencer Fullerton Baird
 Joseph Henry [2]. Fig. 43.
 John Lawrence LeConte
Anne Vallayer-Coster, 1744–1818
 Benjamin Franklin [32]
John Vanderbank, 1694–1739
 Isaac Newton [1, 2]
Charles Amedée Philippe Van Loo, *ca.* 1719–1795
 Benjamin Franklin [2]. Fig. 2.
Robert William Vonnoh, 1858–1933
 William Williams Keen. Fig. 48.
 Henry Charles Lea

Robert William Vonnoh (*continued*)
  William Berryman Scott. Fig. 50.
Thomas Walpole, Jr., 1755–1840
  Benjamin Franklin [29–31]
Samuel Bell Waugh, 1814–1885
  Franklin Bache
  Nathaniel Chapman [2]. Fig. 31.
  George Bacon Wood [1]
Wedgwood pottery
  Sir Joseph Banks
  Robert Boyle
  Charles Robert Darwin
  Erasmus Darwin
  Benjamin Franklin [28, 30, 31, 33]
  William Franklin
  William Temple Franklin
  John Paul Jones
  Marquis de Lafayette [1–3]
  Isaac Newton [3, 4]
  William Penn
  Joseph Priestley [1]
  George Washington [3]
Thomas B. Welch, 1814–1874
  Benjamin Franklin [4]
Benjamin Wilson, 1721–1788
  Mrs. Benjamin Franklin
James L. Wood, ac. 1900
  Joseph Leidy [2]
Ralph Wood, 1716–1772
  Benjamin Franklin [26]
Thomas Woolner, 1825–1892
  Charles Robert Darwin
Joseph Wright of Derby, 1734–1797
  Erasmus Darwin
Robert Wylie, 1839–1877
  Franklin Peale [2]

114

Figures 2–59

The illustrations are arranged in sequence according to date of election of the subject to membership in the American Philosophical Society. Portraits of non-members are inserted at appropriate chronological places, while a few miscellaneous works come at the end.

Fig. 2. Benjamin Franklin [2]. Attributed to Charles Van Loo

FIG. 3. Benjamin Franklin [13]. After Jean Jacques Caffiéri

117

FIG. 4. Benjamin Franklin [15]. By John Flaxman, after Jean Antoine Houdon

Fig. 5. Anne Robert Jacques Turgot, Baron d'Aulne. By Jean Antoine Houdon

119

FIG. 6. Charles Thomson. By William Rush

Fig. 7. David Rittenhouse [1]. By Charles Willson Peale

121

FIG. 8. David Rittenhouse [2]. By Giuseppe Ceracchi

122

Fig. 9. Bishop William White. By George M. Miller

Fig. 10. Benjamin Rush. By Thomas Sully

124

Fig. 11. Marquis de Condorcet. By Jean Antoine Houdon

125

FIG. 12. George Washington [1]. By Gilbert Stuart

FIG. 13. Thomas Jefferson [3]. By Thomas Sully

Fig. 14. Thomas Jefferson [1]. By Jean Antoine Houdon

128

FIG. 15. Thomas Jefferson [2]. By George M. Miller

129

Fig. 16. Shahaka, Mandan Chief. By Charles Balthazar Julien Févret de Saint Mémin.

130

FIG. 17. Alexander Hamilton [2]. By J. Lanelli, after Giuseppe Ceracchi

131

FIG. 18. Marquis de Lafayette [4]. Attributed to E. Luigi Persico

132

FIG. 19. Robert Patterson. By Rembrandt Peale

133

Fig. 20. Samuel Vaughan. By Robert Edge Pine

FIG. 21. John Vaughan [1]. By Thomas Sully

135

Fig. 22. Joseph Priestley [2]. By Rembrandt Peale

136

FIG. 23. Charles Willson Peale. Self-portrait

137

FIG. 24. Caspar Wistar [2]. By William Rush

Fig. 25. Simeon DeWitt. Sculptor unknown

139

FIG. 26. Peter Stephen Du Ponceau [1]. By Thomas Sully

FIG. 27. John Gottlieb Ernestus Heckewelder. Attributed to Gustav Anton von Seckendorff, *alias* Patrick Peale

FIG. 28. Philip Syng Physick. By William Rush

FIG. 29. Friedrich Heinrich Alexander, Baron von Humboldt.
By James Reid Lambdin.

143

Fig. 30. William Tilghman. By Rembrandt Peale

FIG. 31. Nathaniel Chapman [2]. By Samuel Bell Waugh, after Thomas Sully

145

FIG. 32. Robert Maskell Patterson [2]. By James Reid Lambdin

FIG. 33. Nathaniel Bowditch. After Robert Ball Hughes

147

Fig. 34. José Francesco Correa da Serra. By Charles B. Lawrence

148

FIG. 35. Alexander Wilson. By Rembrandt Peale

149

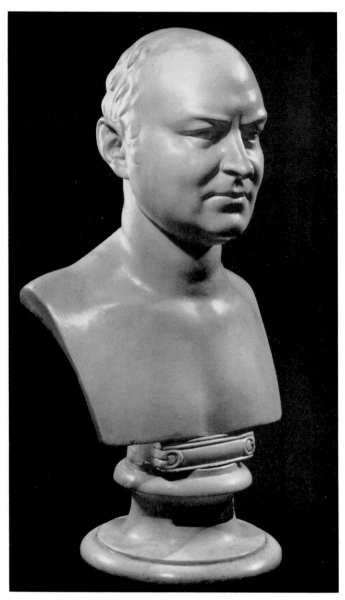

FIG. 36. John Quincy Adams [1]. By Pietro Cardelli

150

Fig. 37. John Kintzing Kane. By Thomas Hicks

151

Fig. 38. Joel Roberts Poinsett. By Thomas Sully

152

FIG. 39. Isaac Lea. By Thomas Pollock Anshutz, after Bernard Uhle

153

FIG. 40. George Bacon Wood. Attributed to Edward Stauch

154

Fig. 41. Alexander Dallas Bache. By Daniel Huntington

155

FIG. 42. Thomas Sully. Self-portrait

156

FIG. 43. Joseph Henry [2]. By Henry Ulke

157

FIG. 44. Frederick Fraley. By Margaret Lesley Bush-Brown

FIG. 45. Louis Jean Rodolphe Agassiz. By Daniel Huntington

FIG. 46. Elisha Kent Kane [2]. By Peter Reniers

160

Fig. 47. Daniel Garrison Brinton. By Thomas Eakins

161

Fig. 48. William Williams Keen. By Robert William Vonnoh

162

Fig. 49. Isaac Minis Hays. By Lazar Raditz

163

FIG. 50. William Berryman Scott. By Robert William Vonnoh

164

FIG. 51. Joseph George Rosengarten. By Julian Story

FIG. 52. Edwin Grant Conklin. By Cameron Burnside

166

FIG. 53. Roland Sletor Morris. By Cameron Burnside

Fig. 54. Thomas Sovereign Gates. By Alice Kent Stoddard

168

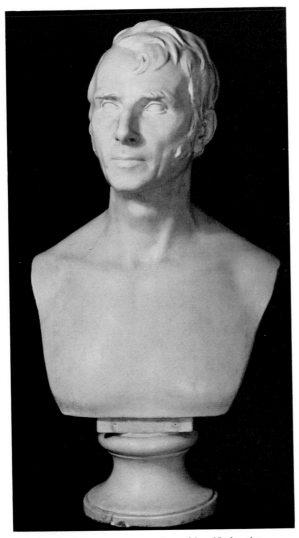

FIG. 55. Unknown man. By unidentified artist

169

FIG. 56. Franklin [5] Urging the Claims of the American Colonies before Louis XVI. By George Peter Alexander Healy

170

FIG. 57. Fairmount Water Works. By Thomas Birch

171

FIG. 58. The Genius of Franklin. By Giulio Monteverde

172

FIG. 59. The American Union. By François, Marquis de Barbé-Marbois

173